Making Every Day Count

A Jewish Doctor Confronts His Illness

by

Joel A. Roffman, M.D.

Mazo Publishers

Making Every Day Count

ISBN 978-1-936778-11-9

Contact The Author:
dr.roffman@gmail.com

Published by:
Mazo Publishers
P.O. Box 10474
Jacksonville, Florida 32247
USA

Website: www.mazopublishers.com
Email: mazopublishers@gmail.com
Telephone: 1-815-301-3559

To my wife Nancy, whose love, reassurance and strong presence lifted me each and every day during my illness, as it lifts me all the days of my life.

❧

To those in medical research, whose insights and persistence have resulted in the development of medications that can effectively treat many illnesses. With proper support for them, medical miracles will continue to be visited upon us.

Table Of Contents

Endorsements

With humanity, wisdom and the insight of religious faith born out of his understanding of Jewish texts and tradition, and graced by his personal faith, sensitivity and extraordinary humility, Dr. Joel Roffman shares with us his journey of faith and fate as he battled lymphoma. This book is a must for anyone who desires to be inspired by one man's optimism and hope in the face of death and how his journey can uplift all of our souls to a life of purpose and meaning.

Rabbi William Gershon
President of the Rabbinical Assembly
Rabbi of Congregation Shearith Israel; Dallas, Texas

Dr. Joel Roffman's cancer memoir, "Making Every Day Count," drew me in on three levels. As a rabbi, I was interested in how Jewish identity gave structure and support to him as he confronted life-threatening illness. As a cyclist, I related to his image of outracing death, even if for just a few seconds. But this book most intensely moved me as a fellow mortal, a person who, while healthy today, is aware that our lives will too soon be over. Dr. Roffman faces this knowledge with a sense of optimism. Why allow our inevitable end to define the meaning of life until that day? He throws himself into life – as a healer, as a husband and father, as a friend and as a Jew. He draws strength from each of these aspects of his life, and returns strength to others. He refuses to be defined by his Crohn's disease or by his lymphoma. Because he has deep purpose in living, he finds courage and strength not only for himself, but also for us, his fortunate readers.

Rabbi Danny Nevins
Dean, Jewish Theological Seminary
Division of Religious Leadership

D r. Roffman has written a book that is at once both deeply personal and universal. He shows us how it is possible to maintain a positive and optimistic attitude while being treated for Stage 4 lymphoma, while recognizing and planning for the possibility that the treatment might not work. He is guided by Jewish values and supported by the Jewish community, just as he is guided by medical values and supported by that community. This will be a valuable book for people facing serious illness, their family and friends, as well as for clergy and healthcare professionals whose job it is to help them navigate the rough waters of that illness.

Rabbi Leonard A. Sharzer, M.D.
Associate Director for Bioethics of the
Finkelstein Institute for Religious and Social Studies
The Jewish Theological Seminary

Foreword

Personal stories bring comfort and inspiration in ways that facts and dictums cannot. They put names and faces to the idea that realistic goals are possible, such as a patient's hope to recover against the odds, or to handle pain gracefully. And stories open a patient's eyes to new ways of thinking about – and tackling – common challenges.

In *Making Every Day Count*, Joel Roffman offers us an intimate view of the private emotions cloaked by his public persona: the moments of terror, anticipating what tomorrow's tests will show; of flagging hope, grappling with survival statistics; of sadness, knowing his cancer journey – and possible death – would impact his beloved wife.

Joel's unique voice makes his cancer biography different from all others. In *Making Every Day Count*, Joel rises from the depths of his cancer journey as a physician to share universal messages of healing found in the teachings of his faith.

Specific insights and lessons that led Joel to comfort, strength and even joy after cancer may help other patients find the same. As I wrote in my foreword to his first book,

Coping with Adversity, "The wisdom of ancient tradition resonates with modern men and women ... The Hebrew Bible offers everyone – Jew and non-Jew, believer and atheist – timeless pearls of healthy perspective on coping with adversity."

I've known Joel since 1981, when his mother-in-law facilitated our first meeting. As an administrative assistant in my husband's office, she obviously did not intend a romantic date. Rather, she thought that my husband and I would enjoy meeting another young couple, especially since Joel and I were physicians. And she was right: dinner was delicious, and the four-way conversation was lively.

But Joel and I were affiliated with different hospitals and attended different synagogues, and our private practices and family responsibilities kept our schedules jam-packed. So our paths rarely crossed, and we slipped into a friendly routine of exchanging holiday greetings and supporting each other's fundraising activities. It was in his New Year's update that Joel told me about his being in treatment for lymphoma.

Joel was well aware of my 25-year cancer journey and writings on survivorship. So, after emailing him that I was praying for him and ready to be of service whenever he called, I left the ball in his court.

His silence through the rest of the winter didn't surprise me, and not just because I knew he enjoyed a wide circle of supportive family and friends. It was Joel's long-standing public persona of irrepressible optimism and can-do fortitude that had forecast he wouldn't need me. For decades, he had managed his Crohn's Disease while caring for patients full-time and training for grueling cycling events. And according to Joel's holiday message, cancer hadn't stopped him either.

But by the end of winter, it did slow him down. In concession to the chemo, Joel explained in his solicitation pitch for his annual 150-mile ride for MS that he'd be "scaling back a bit" and riding only 125 miles. That's Joel.

Just days after his successful springtime ride, I unexpectedly received an email from him. He wrote that he'd completed his chemo and would like "to chat." Assuming he'd bumped into some post-treatment issues, I called him, primed to support his recovery in whatever way he needed me. Imagine my delight when, with his usual energetic cheerfulness, Joel explained that he was calling to invite me to write a foreword for this book.

I accepted, knowing that patients' stories can help other patients.

As expected, many of Joel's experiences have been different than mine. Yet much has been the same. When eating was a chore due to profound nausea, we both ate anyway, perceiving food as medicine. When in pain, we both focused on the needs of others, bringing relief by distracting ourselves with intense, meaningful work. And when faced with the mystery of illness, neither of us ever asked, "Why me?" Hardwired by our medical training to know that life is not fair, we both turned to our Jewish faith to deal with the fact that cancer happened to us.

Whatever your medical challenges, may Joel's personal story and the timeless Jewish teachings help you find comfort, strength and joy on your unique path of healing.

With hope,

Wendy S. Harpham, M.D.
Author of *Happiness in a Storm: Facing Illness and Embracing Life as a Healthy Survivor*

Preface

The Great Migration is the clockwise movement of wildebeests, antelope and zebras in the Serengeti – a large area in Africa that includes parts of Tanzania and Kenya. The animals' migration is a natural phenomenon that follows the cyclical availability of grazing caused by seasonal change. The crossings of the Grumeti and Mara rivers beginning in July are popular safari attractions.

In late July 2014, Nancy and I traveled to Africa to see this spectacular natural phenomenon. Our good friends, Marina and Greg Foster, joined us. A quarter of a million zebras usually precede more than one and one-half million wildebeests and are accompanied by hundreds of thousands of other plains animals, including close to a half million gazelles.

August 5th was the final day of our trip. I awoke at my typically early time and planned to do my exercise routine because this was going to be a very long day of travel, and some exercise to start the day seemed like a great idea. I enjoy exercising, and the logistics of the trip made it difficult to maintain my routine. However, I have a set of exercises that do not require much equipment, and can be done almost anywhere. When I awoke, though, I didn't feel good. I had a vague sense of generalized weakness, and my legs in particular felt weak. They were not painful, but rather felt as though I had already completed a difficult set of exercises. That feeling stayed with me the entire day and for the entire route home. The initial sense of "unwellness" was not new to me, as I will explain later, but I had no idea that this time it heralded a radical turn my life would take over the next seven months.

I was born in the Dorchester section of Boston in 1951. My older brother, parents and I lived in a tenement building. I remember a childhood that was filled with friends and family. I entered a combined undergraduate/medical program at Boston University in 1969, and didn't leave greater Boston until graduating from Boston University School of Medicine in 1975.

My entry into the world of private practice in cardiology began in 1980 and has been a resounding success. Although my wife Nancy was born and raised in Dallas and still had family there, we had been living in Hartford, Connecticut for the four previous years, while I completed my residency in internal medicine and my cardiology fellowship. The decision to move to the metropolitan Dallas area was based on a combination of business and family.

While I grew up in Boston and still had family in the northeast, the business opportunity near Dallas was one that was unmatched in Connecticut and that part of the country. The hospitals were expanding, growth was robust, and there was a yawning gap in cardiology availability in Dallas's northern suburb of Richardson. Cardiology combines my interest in science with a desire to work with people.

In retrospect, becoming a cardiologist seems to have

been a natural and easy decision. But moving from New England to Texas to begin a solo practice was bold and unorthodox.

I am fortunate and grateful that it turned out so well. Without question, the best thing that ever happened to me was marrying Nancy. We have been married since 1976. Nancy grew up in Dallas and graduated from the University of Rochester. The summer before her senior year in college we met in an art course in Boston. We had a long distance romance over the next four years, as she attended the University of Texas Law School after college, and I completed my medical studies in Boston. Following my residency and cardiology fellowship at Hartford Hospital, we moved to Texas.

I began work in solo practice and Nancy raised our two children. Nancy has unyielding devotion to family and is President of the Sisterhood in our synagogue. Sisterhood is an organization made up of Jewish women within the synagogue, providing funds and some services. With her interpersonal skills, her commitment and her intellect, Nancy is perfectly suited to the job.

In February 1982, I began to have symptoms that would ultimately lead to a diagnosis of Crohn's Disease, a chronic inflammatory intestinal disorder that would cause me much discomfort from that point on. The type of feeling that I described earlier – generalized weakness and a sense that my legs were twice as heavy as normal – would often herald exacerbations of the Crohn's Disease, and was followed by sustained periods of abdominal pain. Were these symptoms in Africa a sign that my Crohn's Disease was about to flare up? It had been a long time since I had these symptoms from Crohn's Disease, but the symptoms brought back very bad memories.

Soon after our move to Texas in 1980, we were blessed with a son. In 2001, my son George tragically succumbed to a very aggressive lymphoma that had grown in his brain. George had battled severe Crohn's Disease for 10 years and had been on strong immunosuppressive drugs. The combination of his illness and the medications used to treat it were likely responsible for the cancer.

Many Jews and those of other faiths explain tragedies as an expression of God's will. It is their belief that these and all events are caused by God, in accordance with God's master plan for the universe. In a way, I envy those who share this belief. It must bring great comfort to believe there is a grand plan. Theologically, I am not in full accord with this belief. I do not believe that every occurrence in the universe is orchestrated by a Divine decree. That does not, though, diminish my faith. Nor does it in any way counter the value of the inspirational works and the teachings of Judaism that help me cope with events such as this.

Our daughter Leah was born in 1985, and with her birth, Nancy and I felt that our family was complete. George and Leah provided us with countless hours of mirth and fun through the years.

I am a member of two different synagogues. Congregation Shearith Israel has been my spiritual home since 1985. It is a large shul, whose spiritual leader is Rabbi William Gershon, a very bright and articulate man, who is currently President of the Rabbinical Assembly – an international organization of Conservative rabbis. For years, Shearith held a Shabbat morning service at a Jewish day school near my home.

When Shearith Israel ended its support of this service, the service was terminated. Many of the regular attendees formed another shul so we could continue to meet in a venue closer to our homes and in a more casual setting. Kehillat Chaverim (Community of Friends) was thus born. We have no rabbi serving as our spiritual leader or conducting our worship services. Instead, individual members of the shul lead the various portions of the prayer service. Also, one of the members presents a teaching every Shabbat based on the week's Torah portion. Kehillat Chaverim is where I spend my Shabbat mornings, often after an early breakfast with a friend.

Although I refer to various Jewish sources in this book, I do not in any way consider myself an expert or an authority. Many rabbis would dispute my interpretation of scripture and Jewish teachings, but we all ultimately need to come to an understanding of the Bible that works for us as individuals. While the lessons I derive from these ancient books may differ from others, my Jewish background and identity have been a source of much strength as I have dealt with illness and other challenges in my life. By putting on paper what I experienced and how I coped with it, I hope I can be of help to others.

I began keeping a written record of the sequence of events and of my emotions soon after the diagnosis of lymphoma was established. Keeping a written journal forced me to keep things in perspective as my course unfolded. I generally made journal entries several times a week. My appreciation of my supportive family and friends was heightened as I recounted the acts of kindness shown to me. The wonderful gift of Judaism helped me deal with the path I was faced with, giving me a framework and a viewpoint that fit my medical situation, while allowing latitude of thought, belief and attitude that fit in with my own theology.

The discomfort that I experienced on that morning of August 5th continued for a couple of weeks, eventually migrating to and settling in my upper legs. The generalized feeling of "unwellness" gradually abated, and I actually felt good. But the discomfort in my upper legs continued and became the focus of my concern.

Part One

What Is Causing This Leg Pain?

Thursday, August 21
Leg discomfort that began in Africa.

In preparation for my biannual trip to Mayo Clinic for an appointment with a gastroenterologist, I had lab studies drawn. This was also the beginning of an investigation as to why I was having leg discomfort that, over the prior few weeks, had gradually become more frequent. The vague feeling of "unwellness" had disappeared, but what had begun as leg weakness was now a more defined discomfort in my upper legs. The blood results were fine. There was no hint of an infection or of any major change in my system since the last time I checked, earlier in the year. Nothing seemed amiss, aside from the pain in my upper legs.

As a physician, I often need to investigate the cause of patients' symptoms. Patients who are vague in their answers – those who have difficulty describing a particular discomfort, what triggers their shortness of breath, what brings about their chest pain, etc. often require much time. It's very important to be able to discern exactly what the patient feels and when they experience the symptoms. It is frustrating when the answers are not forthcoming or are vague.

So my leg pain perplexed me. There was no consistent pattern of the discomfort. Sometimes it awakened me at night, but on other nights, there was no pain. On many days, it became intense enough that pain medicine was needed. On still other days, I experienced almost no pain at all. The discomfort was not related to activity, position or time of day. I was able to exercise with no problem.

I continued to believe the leg discomfort would disappear. I thought it might have been a side effect from the malaria prophylaxis I took while in Tanzania, but was unable to find such a symptom related to this medication in my medical reference books. Surely this was just an annoyance that would resolve over time, if only I was patient.

Friday, August 29
Appointment at the Mayo Clinic.

L iving with Crohn's Disease is like having a constant companion who is exceedingly difficult to get along with. This companion sends almost continual reminders of its uncomfortable presence. For reasons that are unclear, the intestines are victims of an inflammatory process, resulting in pain and assorted other miseries. I was first diagnosed with Crohn's Disease in 1982, and at no time have I been free of discomfort for longer than very brief interludes. In the decade or so after I was first diagnosed,

I tried assorted medications, but a major flare-up in 1992 necessitated the use of a stronger medicine – prednisone.

Taking prednisone is akin to making a deal with the devil. Symptoms are relieved quite effectively, but a whole host of short and long-term side effects ensue. For this reason, constant attempts are made to take as small a dose as possible. For years, I constantly juggled my dose. During times of relative freedom from symptoms, the dose would be lowered. But these intervals never lasted very long and inevitably, an increase in pain warranted higher doses.

And so it went, until the end of 2005, when a major flare-up occurred. High doses of prednisone had no effect on my symptoms, and I gradually grew weaker. Finally, this major flare-up of the illness resulted in a perforation – a small tear – of my small intestine. I was in extreme pain for several days. The situation called for the strongest medical weapon available for Crohn's Disease – Remicade.

Remicade is a molecule that attaches itself to other, inflammatory molecules, or enzymes, in the bloodstream, rendering them harmless. The medication is given intravenously every 8 weeks, in a process that takes 3 hours. Other medications similar to Remicade are used in a variety of immune or inflammatory disorders. As a group, they are called monoclonal antibodies – molecules that bind to a specific type of cell. They are now used in many malignancies as well, binding themselves to proteins that are on the surface of malignant cells, resulting in the death of these "bad guys." The advent of monoclonal antibodies has been a major advance in medicine – one that took several decades of research. These agents have made life better for countless patients, and many more are in various stages of development.

The Remicade took a couple of months to work, but work it did. By April, I was beginning to feel much better. My gastroenterologist, Tom Rogoff, told me that Remicade had "announced its arrival!" But in medicine, as in life, there is no free lunch. Because of the way Remicade and its cousin drugs work, the immune system is suppressed, and the patient is at higher risk for serious infections and malignancies. As I frequently tell my patients when discussing treatment strategies for any number of disorders, the practice of medicine entails the constant and repeated weighing of risks and benefits. In my case, I was so sick at the beginning of 2006, I had little choice. I actually felt that a major medical catastrophe was near. The decision to begin treatment with Remicade was an easy one.

Since the spring of 2006 when the Remicade began to work its magic, I have felt much better. There has been much less discomfort and no significant flare-ups of the disease. I have had no hospital stays for the Crohn's Disease and no additional perforations of my small intestine.

As with so many medications, the possible side effects and complications from Remicade can be frightening. When watching television advertisements for this and similar drugs, these warnings are spoken quickly and in an undertone at the end of the ad. We've all seen these ads – we focus on the images of beautiful people enjoying life while the announcer intones the words that the drug can cause ". . . certain type of infections. Some cancers are more common with . . ." But as sick as I was, the relative weights of the risks and the benefits of Remicade led to the only decision that made any sense at all. Clearly, Remicade has been a terrific medication for my condition and I am thankful that it was available when I became so sick in 2006.

My gastroenterologist in Dallas, Dr. Tom Rogoff, has been treating me since I was first diagnosed with Crohn's Disease. He is responsive and bright. But because Remicade in particular and monoclonal antibodies in general represent the "end-of-the-line" treatment for Crohn's Disease, in that there are no other viable options for medicinal therapy, I decided in 2006 to visit the Mayo Clinic. I felt that it was a good idea to be an established patient in a research institution in case the Remicade ultimately failed. I have had an appointment with Dr. Ed Loftus every two years since. It may seem superfluous to see two doctors for the same problem, but it gives me some peace of mind to also be seen at Mayo Clinic. Taking the day off from work to make the trip to Minnesota is worth it to me.

My continuing symptoms, while much less severe than before I began to receive Remicade, have continued to be a reminder that there was a war going on in my body between Remicade and the inflammatory proteins, but the war seemed to be fought with small arms rather than with guided missiles. As far as I was concerned, this low-level conflict could proceed for as long as there were combatants to engage. It was just fine with me. As far as my Crohn's Disease was concerned, that was where we stood in the early fall of 2014.

My upper legs were very uncomfortable on the way to Mayo. I couldn't find a comfortable position during the flight. I discussed the discomfort with Dr. Loftus, but he didn't feel it had anything to do with Crohn's Disease. We speculated on some other possible causes involving my recent travel to Tanzania, such as the antibiotic I took for malaria prophylaxis. The exam and the day were uneventful, but my leg discomfort was beginning to weigh on my mind. The trip home was as uncomfortable as the flight on the way to Mayo earlier in the day.

Thursday, September 25
Rosh Hashanah.

Through most of September, my upper legs were uncomfortable, with pain requiring the use of ibuprofen. It seems that each day with relatively little discomfort was followed by a day of much pain. My internist, Dr. Bill Downs, had disappointed me and many other patients by retiring from medical practice several months ago. The nerve of him! Dr. Downs was everything a patient could want in an internist: he was attentive, smart and caring. For a couple of months, I weighed various options for other internists, but reached no conclusion. If Dr. Downs had still been in practice, I would already have had an appointment with him. My legs were uncomfortable, and the time for investigating the cause of this problem was now. I was still in the process of weighing my options during the High Holidays.

Over the past couple of weeks, I realized I needed to see someone about the leg pain, but on this day in synagogue, I realized that I now had to quickly come to the conclusion of who it would be. It is not like me to ignore health issues. *Rosh Hashanah* (the Jewish New Year) begins a 10-day period of introspection. During this time, the Jewish prayer book envisions that a heavenly court is in session. It is here that God is said to decide on our fate for the upcoming year. Far from being a fatalistic religion, though, Judaism teaches that we have input into what that fate will be.

Activism has always been a prominent teaching of Judaism, whether it is applied to social justice, helping others or helping oneself. Following their escape from slavery, the Israelites were pursued by the Egyptians and reached the Red Sea. In Exodus, we read that, seemingly trapped between the Egyptians and the sea, the Israelites began to pray. But God admonished them, telling Moses that this was not the time for prayer. "Tell the Israelites to go forward!" They then cross the sea. The discomfort in my legs is that same voice. "Stop trying to think about it, Joel. Enough already! Cross the sea! Go and get it checked out!" The gravity of the holidays with its emphasis on self-improvement and renewal served as an impetus for me to make a decision.

Friday, October 3
My choice for a new doctor.

Dr. Michael Tang is new in private practice, having moved to the Dallas area from St. Louis, where he completed his residency at Barnes Hospital and worked as a hospitalist for a couple of years. My friend Greg Foster has a son as well as a son-in-law working at Barnes in a couple of different capacities, and they had only good things to say about Dr. Tang. They reported that he is smart and easy to work with. Until I received Dr. Tang's announcement in the mail, I had been wondering who I would entrust my care to, and was undecided. Dr. Downs would be a tough act to follow. Dr. Tang's office is just up the stairs from mine. Literally, if I drilled a hole in my ceiling, I would find myself entering his office space. So it all appeared to be in place – Dr. Tang seemed to be a smart, communicative internist who was conveniently located. I went to see him today for a doctor-to-doctor visit.

My partner, John Reuter, frequently visits doctors and introduces himself as an option to consult on their patients' cases. Today, I had good reason to make such a visit myself. Patients frequently ask me for the names of internists for their ongoing care. So my visit with Dr. Tang had several purposes. In addition to meeting him as a possible internal medicine doctor for my patients, I was able to leave my business card and some forms he could use if he wished to refer patients to our practice.

Of course, I also was able to try to picture myself as his patient. I knew that he was academically very competent. Was I comfortable speaking with him? The answer was yes. He greeted me with a smile, made eye contact easily, and was very courteous. After leaving him, I went directly to his reception desk and scheduled an appointment to see him next week.

Wednesday, October 8
First appointment with Dr. Tang.

As was the case last week, Dr. Tang greeted me in a warm and friendly way. His style was immediately comforting and put me at ease. He took my medical history, which I had summarized and presented to him in written form and which, except for Crohn's Disease, was rather unremarkable. I also brought him the results from recent blood testing, which also was unremarkable.

Dr. Tang and I discussed what I had written, went over other items on his checklist, and he examined me. There were no items of note.

My legs and hips displayed no obvious abnormalities on exam, and there was no indication elsewhere of any abnormality. My legs were not tender to the touch, and there was no loss of strength. The discomfort seemed to be coming from deep inside. There was no pain when I rode by bike, so it seemed quite unlikely that my leg muscles were the source of the pain.

We decided to proceed with x-rays of the leg bones as well as the hip bones and lower back. Sometimes, Crohn's Disease can affect the joint between the backbone and the pelvis, and Dr. Tang wanted to see if that was the case here.

With a normal physical examination and normal laboratory studies, it seemed unlikely that we would find anything serious, but the bones themselves had increasingly become the focus of attention, and our next step would be in that direction.

October 10, Friday
Well, your bones look fine.

Dr. Tang reported to me that the bone x-rays looked fine. Also, the sacroiliac joints – the area between the backbone and the hip that is sometimes affected by Crohn's Disease – looked fine. There were no obvious infiltrative disorders of the bones, which appeared to have the normal amount of calcium. The discomfort continued, but had actually been better of late. Last Sunday, for instance, I biked 61 miles, and had no need for any ibuprofen either that day or the day after.

Could the process, whatever it had been, be resolving on its own? We chatted about our next step. Although my discomfort had lessened, we both felt that it should not be ignored. For over a month, I had lots of pain. The discomfort clearly wasn't muscular, and Dr. Tang felt that the best test now would be an MRI, a magnetic resonance image, of the bones.

The MRI test is done in the radiology department and assesses an organ's anatomy and, in many cases, its physiology. It uses magnetic fields to form images, so that if there is an abnormal structure within an organ, or if the normal workings of that organ are significantly disrupted, the study will display an image different from what would normally be seen. The test is very sensitive. If even a minor alteration from normal is present, the MRI will display it. The vast majority of MRI results I look at have one thing or another that appears abnormal. I frequently tell patients that hardly anyone has a completely normal MRI. Those of us in medicine sometimes refer to it as a "walking autopsy." So any results would have to be interpreted with that caveat. Still, if we are looking for pathology, an MRI would give us the best chance of finding it. It was scheduled for the following Wednesday.

Wednesday, October 15
MRI.

Surprisingly, my bone pain continued to improve. I had little need for pain medicine since the week before. My mind was filled with conflicting thoughts. An argument raged in my head.

"Maybe this is a self-limited process of some sort. Maybe I should just postpone the study unless and until the symptoms worsen."

"No," the other side of my brain countered. "That pain is real, tough to handle, and has gone on for weeks. I need the MRI study just to be sure there is no major problem."

"Okay, that may be true," the first side continued, "but at my age, MRIs almost always show some sort of abnormality. Am I leading myself onto the 'garden path' of more tests? It is hard to imagine that this is anything serious, given that symptoms had all but vanished and that I biked over 50 miles just a couple of days ago. How could I possibly have anything serious?"

"Don't be a fool! After learning of the results and discussing them with my doctor, I will be able to judge whether further testing is necessary. Don't just sweep that pain under the rug." Back and forth the argument continued.

The outcome of that argument?

After the back-and-forth in my mind, the verdict was in. The "judge" decided that the patient should go ahead and have the MRI. The patient, together with Dr. Tang, could then decide if the results warranted further investigation, or if we could wait and let whatever seems to have caused the pain simply continue to abate.

The test was very long – two and a half hours. It required me to lie still in 20 to 30-minute blocks of time while the images were taken. By late afternoon, the study was completed.

Around the dinner hour, Dr. Tang called me and asked if we could meet in his office early the following morning. I asked if he could give me an idea of the results.

Why wouldn't he simply tell me that everything looked fine? If there was a questionable abnormality on the scan, why wouldn't he simply let me know, and tell me that we needed to meet in person to discuss the next step? He would not, and he was rather insistent that we meet in person.

Certainly, when a doctor insists on meeting a patient in person, the news is not good. To say that I had difficulty sleeping that night would be an understatement. As I tossed and turned, I wondered about the possibilities. Scarring of some sort? The suggestion of an infection? An unclear result that doesn't resolve the issue and that merits further testing?

At this point, the discomfort in my legs had substantially resolved, and I felt quite good overall. Although I expected that with my age and medical history the MRI wouldn't necessarily be completely normal, there must be something more ominous in my report or Dr. Tang would have been more forthcoming on the telephone. It seemed like an eternity before day finally began to break.

Thursday, October 16
"The findings are suspicious for . . ."

I awoke much earlier than was needed. Trying to fall back to sleep was a futile exercise. Would daybreak never come?! I had arranged to meet with Dr. Tang before starting patients in the office, so at least I would not be distracted in my patient care. Finally, at 7:45, I was shown into his office and awaited my fate.

Dr. Tang arrived in the examination room and as always gave me a warm greeting. He rolled his stool next to my chair, took out the report and set before me the typed conclusion of the MRI – a *"high suspicion of metastatic malignancy."* Metastatic malignancy. Cancer that had spread to my bone marrow, meaning that it's widespread and advanced.

I stared at the words as they seared an indelible mark on my brain. My mouth went dry, my heart sped up and I felt suddenly and generally weak.

Metastatic cancer! How can this be? Thoughts raced through my mind – Nancy – she's too young to be alone. Leah – we've been planning her wedding for next fall! How can this be? I stared at the words as if my gaze would change them.

Dr. Tang allowed a moment of silence to pass. He then spoke in a soft voice. His words – his image – are now but a blur. He was quite kind, and pointed out that our mission was to find out as quickly as possible what specific type of malignancy was coursing through the marrow of my pelvis and leg bones. He suggested a CT scan with what is called a contrast agent. This is a specialized x-ray that looks in great detail at the anatomy of the internal organs. The CT scan would cover the chest, abdomen and pelvis. He immediately called the radiology department and was told of an opening this very afternoon, which I quickly reserved.

So many thoughts continued to race through my mind. It was hard even then to process, let alone to recount.

I raced up the stairs to the radiology department, thinking, "How soon will I die? How do I even begin to make sense of all this? Why is the pain in my legs now nearly gone? Could this all be a mistake? Metastatic cancer. From where? How can this be? Will I live to see Leah get married? How can I leave Nancy alone? So is this how my life is going to end? How soon?"

The receptionist in the radiology department gave me two large bottles of the contrast agent which I was to drink around the noon hour, after which I was to report back to the department. I had a patient waiting for me for a treadmill stress test, as it was now 8:30. I immediately called my secretary, Michelle, and told her that I would need to cancel my entire afternoon's patients. My associate, Dr. Reuter, would be able to see any patients that needed to be seen, and the rest would have to be rescheduled. I told her that I needed to speak with her and my other office staff in my consultation room at 9 a.m., immediately after I concluded the stress test on the waiting patient.

Before going into the office lab for my patient, I called Nancy. How I hated to have to make this call! I told her very simply and with as much composure as I could muster that the news was not good and that I might have a malignancy. I asked her to bring her lunch to the office at noon and told her that I would have additional studies in the afternoon. Somehow, I made it through the stress test and was able to keep my mind on the matter at hand.

When I finished, my staff was already gathering in my consultation room, where I looked into each of their eyes and informed them of the results of the MRI. "High suspicion of cancer in my bone marrow . . . More tests must be done quickly . . . Please work with me with respect to my schedule." All of us tried to fight back tears, with only partial success. Though the details were still very preliminary, we all knew the implications. Few additional words were spoken, as the staff made their way back to their desks.

The morning seemed to drag on forever. I couldn't wait to see Nancy, hold her, and tell her that we would do whatever we needed to do to try to get through this. No matter what went wrong in our lives, I always felt better in her presence. She has a wonderful ability to focus on the task at hand while still maintaining a caring and reassuring demeanor. I grabbed my internal medicine textbook at some point and looked up "Metastatic cancer – unknown source." The statistics were grim – too grim to realistically process at that moment. I was immediately sorry I had sought out this information!

After what seemed like an interminable morning, Nancy arrived with her lunch. The food sat mostly uneaten on my desk as we quietly tried to absorb the morning's news. I dutifully drank the contrast as my office staff came in to see Nancy. I tried as best I could to keep an upbeat demeanor, hoping against hope that we would find something treatable. Nancy and I couldn't help but discuss the wedding, and the possibility of a really bad medical course.

The CT scan took only 20 minutes, but as I lay on the exam table, the CT machine whirring in my ears, I kept thinking, "Is this really happening? How can this be cancer?" "Why do I feel better? I've had very little pain in my bones since late last week, yet there is cancer working its way through my bone marrow."

Though I had little definitive information, I needed to call my daughter, Leah, an attorney in New York and my brother, Mark, who does pharmaceutical research in New Jersey. Nancy also called Harley and Linda, her brother and sister-in-law in Dallas, and Sarene, a close cousin in

New York. With the probability of a malignancy, but little definitive information, I only told Mark and Leah that the news was likely not good and that we are probably dealing with some sort of malignancy, but need more information. I told them that whatever is found, we would treat it aggressively and that I would do whatever I possibly could to achieve a good result.

My silent prayer was that in fact, there would be enough we could do to make a good outcome possible. Mostly, I prayed that I would have the strength and the courage to face whatever might come about and to be able to endure whatever treatment was required.

The afternoon was beyond difficult. I did my best to focus on whatever task was at hand, but visions of Nancy and Leah repeatedly sprang into my mind, quickly followed by a lump in my throat.

Dr. Tang again called me during the dinner hour and reported that the CT scan was entirely unremarkable. All of the organs in my chest, abdomen and pelvis looked quite healthy. There was no suggestion of where a primary source of cancer might be. While a "negative" test is almost always good news, the mystery deepened a bit. What, exactly, is in my bone marrow? Dr. Tang felt that it was very important to get tissue from the marrow itself, and a biopsy of the pelvic bone and its marrow was scheduled for the following Monday. A pathologist would then look at the tissue and discover what process was causing the abnormal MRI and, presumably, the leg pain. Again, I was grateful for Dr. Tang's attention and for the early scheduling of the bone marrow biopsy.

At this point, I was heartened. Maybe the malignancy was confined to the bone marrow. While certainly not easily treatable, the prognosis would be better if it was limited in its extent. Of course, once any malignancy affects the marrow, by definition, it is not contained. Cells in the bone marrow, after all, drift out into the bloodstream and can lodge in other organs. If those cells were malignant, their growth might be unrestrained. Still, with no solid organs involved, the prognosis was looking a bit better.

Friday, October 17
Who else to tell?

While I didn't have a definite diagnosis yet, I knew that the biopsy was not going to be normal. Some form of malignancy was present, but it would be some days before I knew exactly what type. Who to call? When to tell them? What to say?

It is very hard to quarantine information. In our hyperconnected world, word travels very quickly. Although I didn't want to make a wide broadcast, I also didn't want my closest friends to hear about this second-hand.

Greg and Marina Foster are close friends, and Nancy and I had traveled to Africa with them last summer. I thought it would be best not to spring this news on Greg while on a bike ride we would share in just a few days, so a call to him was one that I needed to make. A couple of other calls to friends would be enough for today.

Very simply, I recounted the issues with my leg discomfort that led to the MRI, related that the results of the MRI suggested that a malignant process was involved, and that the biopsy would presumably be definitive. With each call, I was choked up, but was able to keep my composure. I also told my friend and associate in the office, John Reuter. John would need to pick up the brunt of the office load for any time I would miss. He was incredibly thoughtful and understanding. It was a great relief to know that my patients would be in expert hands, and would be cared for.

My impatience made the process seem to last forever. Here I was with a possible malignancy, and there was nothing I could do. Why couldn't I have the biopsy sooner? Why couldn't I begin treatment immediately? With all this nervous energy, I needed to take some action. I thought about what type of oncology practice might suit me best, in case I needed to choose. I felt I would do better in a large, university setting rather than in a private practice. I wanted to be in a place where clinical trials were taking place, and where problems of this sort were continually seen. I called the University of Texas Health Science Center and spoke with a nurse, but as expected, she advised me to await the results of my bone marrow biopsy before scheduling an appointment. After we knew the exact cell type of the cancer, she would be best able to direct me to an oncologist who specializes in whatever type was in my system. Medically, there was nothing to do now except to wait.

Saturday, October 18
Synagogue.

On Saturday mornings, I attend worship services at a small synagogue in Dallas, Kehillat Chaverim. Because of my responsibilities there and the closeness I feel with my fellow congregants, I asked if I could make a short announcement near the end of services. I began by saying that the reason for the announcement was because I didn't want my friends hearing news second-hand. I first gave a short background as to the symptoms I had been experiencing for the past month or two. I then told them of the MRI results and how the findings were likely indicative of a malignancy. The room fell as silent as I can ever recall.

As my eyes scanned the room, I could feel the surprise

and concern of those listening. I tried to sprinkle in a bit of humor, telling the group that the CT scan was normal except for my brain, but that Nancy reassured the doctors that my brain had been abnormal for decades, and so this could be ignored. By that point, though, few in the group laughed. I told the congregants that my biopsy would be on Monday, and that I would let several of the members of the shul (synagogue) know the results. They could then pass along the information to the other members.

I had now called my close relatives, told my closest friends and those with whom I attended religious services. There were still others who I wanted to reach out to and would do so in coming days, but I felt that the key people in my life were aware of the situation. Several asked if I wanted them to keep the news to themselves. I told them that if they knew anyone whom they felt should know, then by all means, they could make that call. Also, I didn't want anyone to lie, so it would be okay for them to say what they knew if anyone asked directly about me. On the other hand, I didn't necessarily want the news broadcast, so I asked my friends to use their discretion.

Sunday, October 19
"Thank you . . ."

Sleep is always a bit difficult for me. I have an especially difficult time staying asleep as the morning approaches. The past few nights were, of course, especially hard. I awoke and looked at Nancy, who was still asleep. I was absolutely repulsed by the idea that I was a source of such stress for her. How I wish I didn't have to cause her such worry. The pervasive thought on my mind as I first awaken has been the same for the past few days. Cancer. Me. In my bone marrow.

Before getting out of bed, I did what I do every day, and what I have done for years. I said a prayer. I say the prayer in Hebrew, but the English translates roughly to, "Thank you, sovereign of the universe, for restoring my soul to me today." It is a short, simple prayer expressing gratitude for simply being alive. Although it is a prayer of few words, it helps set the mood for the day. Through the years, there were many days on which I awoke feeling lousy because of my Crohn's Disease. I often experience weakness, fatigue and abdominal pain even before getting out of bed, but this prayer helps me focus on what is beyond me and what I need to focus on as the day begins.

As should ideally be the case with any chronic illness, I have always made an effort to compartmentalize my illness, separating it from other activities, and not allowing it to cloud and dominate my thinking, or interfere with important events and interactions. I admire this ability in patients, many of whom suffer from numerous medical conditions, yet are eager to share joyful family news, and who always come to the office wearing a smile.

Once I say this prayer of gratitude, I immediately think about the day ahead of me. "What events are in store today? Who will come to my office looking for my help? How can I make a difference? Who do I need to reach out to today? There are many people who I can help in some way. So get out of the sack and let's go." Today was no different. The prayer took my mind off things for a bit, but there would be no mental peace on this day. There would not be any such peace for a long time.

Monday, October 20
Bone biopsy.

At last, the weekend was over and we could begin to get closer to a definitive diagnosis. As Nancy and I waited in the holding area of the operating room, my mind raced through some of the various possibilities. My biggest worry about the procedure was that the biopsy would show an "undifferentiated" cancer – one whose exact origin was unknown, but one with a high degree of aggressiveness. This would give us little to treat with except very strong but nonspecific drugs, leaving a poor prognosis and ultimately, only palliative care.

By this time, my bone pain was completely gone! How could there be anything seriously wrong, if the discomfort had disappeared?

Remembering that virtually all MRIs are abnormal in some way, I still held out hope that this was only some inflammatory process that had somehow run its course. After all, just the day before, I rode my bike more than 50 miles. How sick could I be?

The hospital personnel were very courteous and caring. The doctor explained to Nancy and me exactly what the process would entail. I would be asleep, and he would insert a small needle into my pelvic bone at the base of my spine. Through this needle would be withdrawn a sample of my bone marrow. The marrow would be allowed to dry on microscope slides, then treated with special stains, and finally would be viewed by a pathologist. The pathologist would determine whether all the cells of the marrow were normal or whether there were malignant cells among them. The area from which the sample was to be taken was very abnormal on the MRI. The whole procedure would take under an hour.

I had visions of the pathologist reporting that he didn't

have enough of a sample to make a firm diagnosis and told the doctor to be sure he got enough tissue (though he certainly did not need my coaching!). The procedure went very smoothly. I awoke from the anesthesia very quickly, and in fact remember being wheeled out of the operating room. Now the wait was on. The report would go to my internist, Dr. Tang. Because of the special tissue stains and preparation, it would take a couple of days for the report to be available.

I made an agreement with Dr. Tang that whether the news was good or bad, he would deliver it in person. It would have been excruciating for him to tell me by telephone that I needed to come to his office the following morning. This would force me to wait all night knowing that bad news was to follow. When the MRI report became available last week, he asked me to come to his office the following morning, where I was to receive the horrible news. On the other hand, he told me of the normal CT report by telephone. Dr. Tang agreed with this plan and sure enough, by late Wednesday, the report was in his hands, so we arranged to have an early morning talk on Thursday.

Thursday, October 23
Diagnosis.

At last, the day of reckoning was here. There would either be bad news upon which to act definitively, or good news that would enable me to put all this behind me. As I ate breakfast, I was still engaged in full-blown rationalization. I had been working out regularly and spent long days in the office. I experienced no loss of energy or appetite. I felt fine. How could this be anything but a benign inflammation of some sort? Maybe it is some type of infection that had run its course.

Possibilities raced through my mind as I left home to meet with Dr. Tang. Wishful thinking displaced more rational thoughts. The MRI strongly suggested that a malignant process was involved, but I continued to focus on and anticipated more benign scenarios. Time seemed to stand still as I waited for 7:45 – the time at which we were to meet.

"Surely, with no continued discomfort, there couldn't possibly be a malignant process going on," I thought, as I climbed the stairs of the office building. As Dr. Tang came into the exam room, my heart was beating so fast, I felt as though I was climbing a steep hill on my bike. My mouth was as dry as sandpaper. Dr. Tang greeted me warmly, again pulling his stool close to my chair. He looked me directly in the eye, and told me the news.

The biopsy showed that I had lymphoma. Lymphoma is a form of cancer that involves cells of the immune system called lymphocytes, a type of white blood cell. Specifically, my type is called "large B-cell lymphoma." The cancerous cells had spread through the marrow of my pelvic and leg bones. There was no hedging or doubt. It no longer mattered that I felt fine. It no longer mattered that all the other studies – lab, CT, x-rays – were essentially normal. Lymphoma is a malignancy and must be treated aggressively. I told Dr. Tang that my preference was to be treated at UT Southwestern, and that I had made preliminary contact with them. I anticipated needing the pathology slides and a copy of the MRI scan so that the doctors at Southwestern could review all the data. As always, Dr. Tang was very kind and assured me that he and his staff would do whatever they needed to do in order to expedite the process.

While speaking with Dr. Tang, I could feel my mood changing by the minute. Though this was not good news by any stretch of the imagination, at least I now had a firm diagnosis and a firm mission. The enemy had been identified, and the course was now clear. I hurried downstairs and told the office staff. This time, I was much less emotional, and the staff took their cue from me. They understood that we were going to have ongoing schedule changes and assured me that they would do whatever was required. I again immediately called Nancy. As always, Nancy was more comforting than I could have hoped or asked. She was supportive and resolute. I told her my plan – I would call UT Southwestern and get an appointment as quickly as I could.

I immediately made the call to the oncology center at UT Southwestern and navigated through several contacts before speaking with someone who could direct me to the proper oncologist and schedule an appointment. The earliest appointment I could get was the following Tuesday, but all things considered, that was pretty quick. The Baylor pathologist would need additional time to do more studies on the microscope slides that contained specimens from my bone marrow, and I needed a couple of days to get the slides to UT Southwestern for review by their own pathologist. I was pleased that in this way, two sets of eyes would review the pathology. Realistically, there would not have been much good in having an appointment before all the data was in the hands of an oncologist.

I was grateful to have a busy schedule because it left little time to think. I called Leah and told her the news. I told her of my plans to be seen at the medical school and that we would treat the cancer very aggressively. While I didn't know the survival statistics, I told her I was confident of a good outcome and would do whatever I could to make it so. We would make no changes in the wedding plans! Leah's fiancé, Ross, called with a heartfelt and kind expression of support. My brother was on an airplane at the time, so I would have to wait until later to speak with him directly.

Sunday, October 26
Reactions from friends.

One doesn't have to go through treatment for cancer to empathize with those who are ill. Reactions from people with whom I shared the news of my illness ran the gamut from sincere concern and offers to be of help and support to self-directed "war stories" about their own illnesses.

I had a friend respond to my news by telling me of their father, who battled lung cancer before succumbing to the disease, and another who was eager to remind me that she had breast cancer a decade earlier. In neither case was there a quick effort to circle back to me. The people in question were simply responding to my case with a case of their own. I suppose these were attempts to be supportive, clumsy though they were, but a person needs to be tone-deaf to respond to someone's hardship with a story of their own.

The recommendations that follow are based not only on my own experience, but also from observing and understanding what patients need. When learning of a friend's illness or hardship, it is a time to put yourself in your friend's shoes. Listen. Care. Help.

What to say: "I'm so sorry this has happened." The word "sorry" has a couple of meanings. It doesn't only mean regret for one's actions. It is also an expression of sorrow. This word, or another like it, should be the first thing you say.

What not to say: "Oh, I had __ (fill in the blank with your particular illness), and this is what happened . . ." This is not about you! This is about a friend whose life has just been upended and needs your support, not your own tale of woe. The same applies to relating the story of an acquaintance who may have had the same problem. Few people want to hear about others at this particular time. There may be time when a support group is recommended, or for your friend to have conversations with others in order to share experiences, but this is not one of them.

A simple test: if a friend says to you, "I'm so tired – I've been having trouble sleeping lately." What should your response be? Too many people will respond by immediately recounting their own problems with sleep. Instead, listen to your friend. Is there a reason for her sleep problem? Is there something troubling on his mind? Respond to people's needs, not your desire to talk about yourself. We must avoid the approach of, "Can you top this?" No one has a corner on the market when it comes to misfortune. If friends share their misfortune with you, the proper response is one of sensitivity and empathy, not a self-directed story about your own troubles.

Here is another recommendation. When you learn of a friend's hardship, rather than saying, "Let me know if there is anything I can do." Offer one or two specific things, such as, "Do you need transportation to and from your treatments? If so, know that I'm here for you – please call if I can take you and bring you home. I would love to be able to help" Or, "I'm happy to prepare a meal for you and your family. I know how schedules can get jumbled during treatment. Just give me the word." Or maybe, "Please let me know if I can pick up some things at the store for you." We must always remember that to *have* a friend, we must *be* a friend.

Tuesday, October 28
Oncology appointment with Dr. Naina.

I chose UT Southwestern for my cancer care because of its reputation and large volume of cancer patients.

The campus is a daunting presence, with one large building after another. The check-in area reminded me of a small train station, with rows of chairs and several clerks asking the question-of-the-day: "Have you traveled to West Africa in the last 21 days?" (The recent Ebola scare has affected all levels of medical care.) The oncology clinic waiting room's obligatory facemask was a reminder that people weren't here for well-patient check-ups. I was now definitely among the medically compromised.

Dr. Harris Naina is an oncologist who specializes in lymphoma, and he would be caring for me. He entered the room and greeted Nancy and me in a professional and friendly manner. Together, we reviewed the MRI images, and he pointed out the abnormal shadows caused by sheets of cancerous lymphocytes. I was a bit taken aback when he immediately started talking about the chemotherapeutic regimen I would be taking. Given my lack of current symptoms, I thought that maybe, just maybe, the condition could be treated with a less toxic combination of drugs than had been set out.

Dr. Naina gently but firmly told me that with cancerous cells in my bone marrow, I was considered to be in Stage 4 (the most advanced stage). There was no margin for error and no viable alternative to full-bore multi-drug chemotherapy. Dr. Naina felt that it was indeed unusual for my symptoms to have almost completely disappeared, but the pathology left no question about the diagnosis. Of course, I understood.

Beyond stating that he felt confident of a good result, Dr. Naina and I did not discuss actual statistics. It really didn't matter at that point. I've been in medicine long enough to understand that diseases don't read textbooks. Every case is different. If the statistics for recovery were unfavorable, I would have confidence to see myself as one of the good responders. On the other hand, if the statistics were in my favor, I would still have realized that there are no guarantees. I understood generally that most patients taking the combination of drugs that I was to receive have a good response, and that tidbit of information will have to suffice for now.

It's actually a formidable task to attempt to find out what my chances of recovery are. Several parameters factor into the exact odds of success for a particular person. These include age, extent of the cancer, specific cell type, and the general medical condition of the patient. Then, the numbers are further broken down into "survival" and "event-free survival," with the former representing all those who are alive after the specified time, no matter what their medical condition might be, and the latter, which counts only those who have had no recurrence of the tumor after the time.

For B-cell lymphomas, the numbers for me can be framed as either good or bad news, depending on one's viewpoint (like so many other things in life!). The overall five-year survival rate for those with lymphoma is quoted at 75%, while the event-free rate is around 50%. In other words, while I most likely will survive for the next five years, my chances of a long-lasting remission are around "50-50." In general, my worldview is an optimistic one. I tend to look at the bright side of situations. When I first read those statistics, my thought was that I have a cancer that is quite treatable, with around half of all patients cured of the malignancy. I was heartened. I'm not a Pollyanna, though. I fully realize that half of patients like me have a recurrence, and a quarter of them aren't alive in five years. This is certainly not a rosy outlook. Additionally, the actual numbers may be a bit worse, because I am in Stage 4, and the statistics quoted include those with less advanced disease.

Dr. Naina brought up the issue of my Crohn's Disease. Although people with Crohn's Disease have an abnormality with their immune system, there is a strong possibility – maybe even a probability – that my lymphoma was directly related to the use of Remicade. I will no longer be able to receive this medicine. Dr. Naina told me that in his experience, patients undergoing chemotherapy seem to have a lessening of their Crohn's symptoms, and that we probably will have several months to consider an alternative medication regimen for my intestinal disease. Still, this is certainly bad news, as the Remicade made a marked difference in my symptoms for the past eight years.

We then discussed a time frame for an additional study – a PET scan that would more accurately depict the extent of tumor involvement and would serve as a baseline for comparison to gauge the effects of treatment. A PET (Positron Emission Tomography) scan is performed in the nuclear medicine department. It is an imaging study that produces a three-dimensional picture of functional processes in the body. The test is very sensitive, and many different diseases and causes of inflammation can cause the test to be abnormal. In my case, we would be looking for the exact extent and density (concentration) of the cancerous cells.

The scan would be done this Friday, after which I would immediately meet again with Dr. Naina to review the results. The chemotherapy was to begin the following Wednesday. Ariel, Dr. Naina's nurse, presented me with a written schedule before I left the clinic.

Dr. Naina told me that his oncology group's protocol was to do a repeat PET scan after my second round of treatment. This will be a critical test in terms of refining the chances of my survival. If many cancerous cells remain in my system at that time, the odds of survival drop considerably. On the other hand, if the tumor is essentially gone, the odds of an "event-free survival" will be more than 90%.

In the meantime, we discussed the necessity to have a small cylindrical plastic receptacle – a port – placed under my collarbone and into a large vein in my chest, through which the chemotherapy drugs would be injected. This port would spare my veins the caustic effects of the drugs, and would be much more comfortable. The insertion of the port is done under general anesthesia. We needed to schedule this procedure through the radiology department. I called my office nurse, Gayle, and asked if she could try to arrange the insertion of the port at Baylor Hospital, right near my office and home. With any luck, we would be able to do it within the next couple of days.

On the drive home, the enormity of what happened to me and what was about to happen settled in. I had gone from uncertainty and anxiety about my symptoms, to disbelief about having cancer, to a resolve to move ahead as quickly as possible to get it treated. Now, everything was scheduled. I had time to catch my breath. In the car, Nancy tried to be positive and cheerful, but I wasn't ready for that, at least not yet. While I knew I would rally emotionally, I needed just a bit of time to feel sorry for myself. Even though "things could be worse" – I could have had a more devastating malignancy in my bone marrow, for example – things could certainly be a whole lot better as well. My disease is life-threatening, and its treatment involves powerful medications with side effects that are difficult to manage and complications that are possible. I needed just a bit of time to let this all settle.

Wednesday, October 29
Medication port inserted.

As usual, Gayle, who has worked with me for more than 30(!) years, was terrific and was able to schedule the procedure exactly when we needed it. As with the bone biopsy, the first question upon checking in to the hospital involved travel to West Africa. I now answer the question even before it is asked. The radiologist explained how he would insert a catheter into a vein in my neck, "tunnel" it under my skin, and attach it to the plastic port that would serve as the conduit for the chemotherapy. The port would be visible as a bulge under my skin, just beneath my collarbone.

As the radiology technologist scanned my neck with an ultrasound probe to be sure my vein was in its expected location, I asked her to place the probe over my carotid artery, which sits right next to the vein. As I hoped, the carotid artery was free of any visible plaque. There was no evidence of any hardening of the arteries in the carotid vessel. Though the picture was only of a portion of this artery, there was heartening for me – a slim, fit cardiologist! The way this bit of good news was noted and received by me got a chuckle from the assembled radiology and nursing staff in the operating room.

I awoke quickly from the anesthetic with no ill effects, and was now ready for the army of drugs to charge into my body and do battle with those bad cells. Aside from forming the promised bulge just under my collarbone, the presence of the port gave no evidence of its presence. It was ready to serve as the conduit through which the drugs would be infused.

Friday, October 31
PET scan. Discussion with Dr. Naina.

My PET scan was scheduled early in the morning, and I was then to meet with Dr. Naina to go over the results. As was the case with the CT scan I had, there was a contrast agent for me to drink. This time, because of radioactive material used for the test, I was confined to my own room in the radiology department for an hour before the actual scan. A small intravenous line was inserted in my arm for the injection of the chemical that would attach to the malignant cells. The clusters of cancerous cells would then be highlighted on the scan, and their actual range and concentration could be gauged. The scan itself was quick, and was attended to by a friendly and attentive technician. Immediately after the scan was finished, I went to the oncology department for my appointment, where Dr. Naina was to meet with me after an hour or so.

Dr. Naina was prompt. He sat at the computer screen, and after a few keystrokes, my PET scan appeared. The scan was very abnormal. The malignant clusters of cells lit up in the bones of the pelvis and upper legs much as an ornamental tree is lit in multiple places. The spread of cancerous cells was extensive. Dr. Naina was not surprised, because the MRI from last week hinted at the extent of the cancer. Looking at the scan, though, was very disconcerting.

It is obvious that much needs to be done. The goal, of course, is to eradicate each and every one of those cancerous cells, while doing as little damage as possible to all of my normal cells. This cannot be done with absolute precision – that's why chemotherapy brings along with it many side effects. Drugs are becoming more specifically directed to cancer cells, though, and as I will learn, I will be receiving one of those agents as well as the older, more traditional ones.

In addition to the abnormal findings in the bones of my legs, there was a small but worrisome area of possible tumor involvement in my stomach. Dr. Naina wanted to know for certain if this represented spread of the lymphoma and arranged for a biopsy of this area immediately before my first chemotherapy treatment the following Wednesday.

Still, the test was somewhat encouraging. Although involvement of the bone marrow placed me in "Class 4," the fact that it might not involve other organs gave me hope that it would be easier to eradicate.

It would be a long few days before my first treatment, and I was glad that Nancy and I had special plans for the weekend.

Saturday, November 1
At my brother's house in New Jersey.

This would be my last weekend out of town for at least several months. Because of the possible complications of chemotherapy, I was to remain home until treatment was completed and my blood counts, which would be abnormal during treatment, were back to normal.

My brother Mark lives in New Jersey with his wife, Ina. They had planned on a dinner at their home with Nancy and me, and also with our daughter Leah and her fiancé, Ross. Some of Ross's family would also be there. I assured Mark that there would be no need to alter the plans. We anticipated this time with them for several months. My brother and I have a close relationship. He is several years older than me, and has always played the role of "big brother." Perhaps the early death of our father helped foster this sense of responsibility. Mark was ready to travel to Texas to be with me during my treatment, but we decided that it made more sense for him to wait until Thanksgiving, come with Ina, and spend a few days with us then.

Even in adulthood, Mark has always taken his role of big brother very seriously, and has been unfailingly protective and caring. He took the news of my lymphoma very hard, but I know it did him good to see me looking fine and heading into treatment with a positive outlook. I have always been able to count on him for a willing ear, lots of support and encouragement, and an abundance of good humor through the whole process. His sons, Gary and Jeremy, will also be in touch, as they always are, in good times and bad.

The dinner was fun, and to my relief, there was very little discussion of my illness. I would have felt very uncomfortable for it to dominate the evening, which was, after all, for Leah and Ross. I was quite willing to talk with various members of the family about what was in store for me, but felt awkward discussing it in a group setting, especially with Ross's family, whom I had not yet even met.

Sunday, November 2
Dinner with Leah and Ross.

The day after dinner at my brother's home, Nancy and I had dinner with Leah and Ross at a restaurant very close to our hotel in New York City. We chose this particular restaurant in order to see if it would be a suitable place to have a celebratory dinner the night before Leah and Ross's wedding next October. To my surprise, Leah told me that she would be coming to Dallas for my first chemotherapy treatment next Wednesday, and she gave me a present – a portable DVD player with a set of DVDs about the history of Fenway Park – home of the Boston Red Sox. (I grew up in Boston and suffered through frustration and many well-documented team failures with them for decades. At last and to my utter amazement, they finally won the World Series in 2004. Although I now root also for the Texas Rangers – my current hometown team – I am still a fan of the Red Sox as well.)

Leah has been a joy and source of deep pride. She was an honor student at Tufts University, and then graduated Boston College Law School. She works in New York City and is engaged to be married next fall. Ross is everything I could possibly want for my daughter: he is loving, smart and engaging. The cantor from the synagogue where Ross had his bar mitzvah will perform their marriage ceremony.

My first reaction was that Leah's planned visit was unnecessary – I would be just fine during the treatment, and I had enough reading and other media to keep my mind occupied. I realized, though, that this was an act of love and caring. It meant a lot to Leah to be able to show her love, and the trip would help reassure her that I could handle the treatment. So instead of protesting her generous gesture, I told Leah how much this meant to me and that her visit would surely help brighten my day, making the hours of treatment pass more quickly. I've learned that sometimes, allowing someone to give of themselves is itself a good deed. A good example of this takes place regularly in my synagogue in Dallas.

At Congregation Shearith Israel, we have a program that provides meals for those who are in need – typically a short-term need following an illness or surgery. We typically bring dinner to the home of the individual several times a week, usually for a couple of weeks. The program is not intended to fulfill all of the dietary needs of the congregant, but offers some relief to family members while demonstrating how much we care for the recipient of the meals.

I have coordinated this "Mitzvah Meals" Program since its inception in 2009. The word *mitzvah* in Hebrew has a double meaning. It means both a commandment and a good deed. Jews are thus commanded to do good deeds. "Mitzvah Meals" gives volunteers this opportunity.

Over the past five years, our volunteers have served more than 500 meals to congregants, and the program is ongoing. The character and innate goodness of the volunteers is demonstrated by the fact that they make their offer to bring a meal even before knowing who the congregant is. It is all set up anonymously, with no personal information given out until I arrange a final schedule.

When I make contact with the potential recipient, I am sometimes told that the individual doesn't want to be a bother. They don't want to inconvenience anyone by having them prepare and deliver a meal. I explain to these congregants that the volunteers offer to provide these meals because they want to, and because it enables the volunteer to feel that they have helped someone.

Allowing someone to do something nice and thoughtful is actually a good deed in itself. In this way, the volunteers are playing a major role in helping someone in need. In Hebrew, the action of bringing healing and comfort is a form of what is called *tikkun olam* (healing the world). The person in need is actually performing a good deed by enabling him or herself to be helped.

So by not arguing with Leah about either the gift or her upcoming trip to Dallas, I was enabling her to help me, and to show her love for me.

Part Two

Coping With Chemotherapy

Wednesday, November 5
Endoscopy and my first chemotherapy treatment. Finally!

Nancy and I arrived for my endoscopy shortly after 5:00 a.m. The admitting procedure was now very much routine. "No, I have not recently been to West Africa!" Soon, an intravenous line was threaded into my vein, an anesthesiologist arrived, introduced himself, and asked the usual questions about any reactions I had to previously used anesthetic agents. Dr. Harris, the gastroenterologist, briefly introduced herself and understood the tight time schedule we were under, with my first round of chemotherapy scheduled to begin just a short time after the endoscopy was completed. She knew exactly what we were looking for in my stomach and would take biopsies of the area.

Before I was fully aware of what had happened, I was waking up and was being rolled onto the elevator so that

Nancy could transport me across campus, in time for my first chemotherapy infusion. The procedure was very fast and uncomplicated. The short-acting anesthetic wore off completely even before I could fully dress myself. Dr. Harris reported to me that she saw nothing suspicious, but she biopsied the area anyway. It is likely that the area in question on my PET scan simply represented an unusual fold within the stomach and not a spread of the cancer.

Different types of cancer call for different types of treatment. Not only that, but the specific type of cell within the organ system in question mandates a distinct course of therapy. Some cancers are best treated by an operation that removes the entire block of cancerous cells. Others respond to radiation, while surgery or chemotherapeutic drugs might be less effective. Still others require the use of drugs that kill the cancer cells. Unfortunately, most of these drugs also kill innocent cells. The key is finding the right balance – killing the greatest number of cancer cells while leaving enough healthy cells so that the healthy cells that survive can regenerate and the patient can survive the treatment.

Even for a particular regimen of chemotherapy, the individual drugs used are very specific. For instance, leukemia refers to cancer of the blood cells, but the specific combination of drugs used in treatment depends on which cell type within the blood has become cancerous. In a similar way, not all lymphomas are alike. Some are very slow growing. Depending on the patient, these may warrant a wait-and-see approach.

B-cell lymphomas, the type in my bone marrow, are lethal when left untreated. While medicine continues to offer more effective choices, the current standard of care calls for an aggressive combination of chemicals – five, to be exact – that are given every three weeks over several months. Beginning today, I will start receiving this combination. It will be followed by the same combination of drugs until I have received the treatment six times. I will come to a building within the hospital complex – the infusion center – to receive each round of chemotherapy.

Although my workup has proceeded in a very efficient manner, it has seemed like an endless succession of testing, awaiting results, having discussions, reading, and worrying. Now at last, the medications are infusing through the indwelling port I had inserted last week.

The regimen for my particular type of lymphoma is called R-CHOP, with each letter representing a particular drug. The last four drugs in the regimen have been used for years, but one of the components, the "R" – stands for rituximab and is a relative newcomer to the cocktail. Similar to the Remicade that I had taken for Crohn's Disease, rituximab is a monoclonal antibody that is administered intravenously and acts specifically against the cancerous lymphocytes that have invaded my body – the so-called B-lymphocytes.

The "C", "H", and "O" are the first letters of older cancer drugs that kill cells in a less selective way, killing normal cells with the malignant ones. Because cancer cells multiply so quickly, a greater proportion of cancerous cells than normal cells are destroyed. But because many normal cells are affected, changes in the body become apparent. For instance, the cells that produce hair multiply quickly, and so are typically harmed by chemotherapy drugs, resulting in hair loss.

The first four of these drugs are given intravenously every three weeks. Even before the first drug is infused, a medication to prevent and treat nausea is given, also by an intravenous infusion. So altogether, I was to receive five different medications. The "P" in the regimen is prednisone, an oral medication that I am to take at home for five days, beginning on the day I receive the intravenous regimen.

One drug followed another in a seemingly never-ending

parade. I silently cheered them on – "Let's get those B-cells! Kill them off!" Although the day was long, it felt very productive. We were now actually treating the lymphoma, and were taking the first concrete steps toward my recovery. Shawn, my nurse, was outstanding. He explained how long each of the medications would take to infuse, and what I could expect. "This one will eventually make your fingers and toes tingle . . . This one will turn your urine red." Shawn's comments were helpful but unsettling.

With all the medical visitors – the PA (physician's assistant), the oncology fellow (a doctor in his final years of training), the oncologist, the nurse assistant, etc., and with the frequent taking of my vital signs by Shawn, the morning seemed to go very quickly. Nancy was to pick up Leah from the airport in the early afternoon; they would then come directly to the hospital. After lunch, I took a nap, and by the time I awoke and read for a while, Nancy and Leah joined me for the remainder of the treatment.

The toughest part of the day and of the whole experience in dealing with cancer was the fact that my family was suffering right along with me. I wish I could have gone to some far-off place, taken my medicine, and then returned home to my loved ones. Here was Leah, home from New York for a single day just to be by my side. For weeks, every time I thought of the mental anguish my loved ones suffered because of my illness, I had to fight back tears. But the best gift I could give them was to maintain as cheerful an attitude as possible, to appreciate their love, and to get well again.

Upon the completion of my treatment, Ariel, Dr. Naina's nurse gave me a packet of information about the drugs that are being used in my chemotherapy regimen. Each sheet in the packet listed the potential side effects and dangers of the individual drugs. Without reading the sheets in the packet, I placed the packet into the bag that had my reading material for the day. The next morning I placed the packet into a cabinet in my office, still unread.

I had no desire to read about the possible side effects of all these medications. I understand how subjective side effects can be, and I don't want to be anticipating what I might feel, knowing that the anticipation in itself can heighten awareness. There is no doubt that the medications all have various side effects. These are strong chemicals with far-reaching effects in the body.

Receiving chemotherapy is like walking on a narrow bridge. The idea is to "thread the needle" and stay upright on the bridge. The combination of medications should be strong enough to overwhelm and kill any cancerous cells, while not so strong as to critically injure me. It would serve no purpose to know ahead of time all the symptoms that might arise, and all the consequences that might befall me.

I simply asked Ariel, "What might happen that I should report? When do I need to call?" The nurse responded that if I run a fever, I shouldn't even bother to call, but rather come directly to the hospital, because I would need to be started immediately on strong antibiotics. The chemotherapy drugs will lower my white blood cell count and will result in a high susceptibility to infection. This would require immediate attention.

Ariel's instructions were fine with me. Whatever I feel, I will attribute to the drugs, and simply deal with it. It's not as though fatigue, tingling of the fingers or any of a number of side effects will alter my need for these drugs. I intend to simply make a mental note of what apparent side effects I experience and report them at my next session with the doctor. If they can easily be remedied, of course that would be great. If not, so be it. Meanwhile, the packet of information will sit in a closed cabinet, unread.

Thursday, November 6
Yet one more drug.

I was eager to get to work today, doing what I do – taking care of patients, then going home to spend time with Nancy. I awoke with no side effects from yesterday's treatment, although Shawn told me that the anticipated nausea and weakness may not occur for a couple of days.

There is yet one more medication that I will take as part of my regimen. Tonight, I will give myself an injection of a drug used to stimulate the bone marrow's production of granulocytes – the variety of white blood cells that immediately fights germs as they enter the body.

It may seem paradoxical that the chemotherapy kills the same cells whose production we will be encouraging. But the cancerous cells are of a different type – lymphocytes. And while the chemotherapy kills all types of white blood cells, these granulocytes grow and work differently from lymphocytes. The injection will shorten the amount of time my granulocyte count is low, thereby lowering my risk of contracting a severe infection following each round of chemotherapy.

Often, this drug is administered in a clinic, but it is not essentially different from insulin. A very small needle is used, and the injection is virtually painless. I suppose the reason for its administration to be more tightly controlled is the cost of the drug – it runs upwards of $2,000 a shot!

I have patients who view the taking of any medicine as a sign of weakness, and who I can predict will call the very day after a new prescription is given, reporting many of the side effects listed on the internet. My own view of the use of medicine is different from that of many of my patients. Admittedly, my situation is different from treating patients with, for instance, blood pressure medicine. Certainly, high blood pressure is not as immediately life-threatening as cancer, and there are often alternative choices of medicines that we can make, with the same beneficial result. Still, many patients will report to me that they "hate medicine" and will do most anything to avoid its use.

The use of medications should be viewed as a sign of strength rather than a sign of weakness. We are empowered to treat conditions that only a generation or so ago were not treatable. President Franklin Roosevelt died from a stroke caused by untreated hypertension. Albert Einstein died of a ruptured abdominal aortic aneurysm. These are conditions that are now amenable to definitive treatment. Why not take advantage of these medical advances?

There are many reasons why we live longer and are healthier than prior generations. Medications that have been developed over the decades are one of those reasons. I'm grateful that we have medications that can treat my cancer, and am certainly willing to accept whatever side effects I experience. The most important thing is to live.

Friday, November 7
The hair comes off.

M y oncologist told me that my hair would fall out a few weeks after beginning treatment. It really didn't take very long at all for me to decide that I would be proactive. I had a haircut appointment scheduled for today anyway, and would take care of this issue right now. "Keith," I told my barber, "I will give you the details while you're cutting, but I have lymphoma and will be receiving chemotherapy, and I want a really close cut, so I don't have to watch my hair fall out." Keith was great. "You don't know how many times I've done this. And maybe the short haircut is a good omen, because every one of my customers has recovered."

With that, the clippers came out, and as I told Keith my story, my hair was shorn as though I was just another sheep. I chatted away as my hair fell to the floor in large clumps. I realize that some of this (maybe most of it!) is rationalization, but I immediately liked the look! No more hairbrush. No more hair dryer. Good heavens – I actually liked the style!

"Much more aerodynamic," I would tell my friends. "Wait until you see how much faster I am on the bike with no hair to slow me down!" I had Nancy take a photo of me with my cell phone, and I sent it off to my office staff and a couple of friends. Of the many issues revolving around the diagnosis and treatment of cancer, hair loss is one that I don't wish to occupy my mind. Others are far more consequential.

Saturday, November 8
Weight gain? There must be a mistake!

I usually weigh myself once every week or so. My weight rarely fluctuates by more than a pound or two in either direction. I hadn't weighed myself in a couple of weeks and when I got on the scale today, I expected that I would be down a bit because of recent events. To my surprise, the scales told me that I gained 5 pounds! I was so surprised that I actually got off the scale and repeated the weigh-in. Same result.

One of the medications in my "cocktail" is prednisone – a strong anti-inflammatory medicine. Although I didn't feel bloated, I quickly realized the weight gain wasn't anything more than water retention from the prednisone. Once I stop this medicine in a couple of days, I anticipate eliminating the extra water. The gain in weight is just one of the many changes I've noticed over the past few days. Another is mild nausea that seems to peak in the early morning, but that has also awakened me from sleep a couple of times. I also have a very mild "dizziness" that is actually better described as an equilibrium issue. My balance seems slightly less stable. This comes and goes, but is noticeable during much of the day.

Yes, there are some definite changes going on. The chemicals are not only killing the B-cells, but are coursing their way into and through other organs. My appetite isn't normal, but hasn't yet declined to the point that I'm indifferent to meals. The infusion nurse told me to expect this beginning several days after my treatment. I will plan to continue to weigh myself every week or so, and I realize that maintaining good nutritional status is important as I battle the lymphoma. I've told patients in a similar situation to think of food as medicine. "You don't need to be hungry. Hunger is a luxury," I tell them. "Just eat."

Sunday, November 9
A bike ride.

One of my very favorite weekly activities is to ride my bicycle on Sunday mornings. I often meet with a friend for part of the ride, but on this ride I was alone. I typically leave home soon after dawn breaks, usually even before the sun actually rises, and bike all morning. My ride generally covers between 45-60 miles, and sometimes even more. Today's ride, though, had a special poignancy to it. It was my first ride since my diagnosis.

With colder weather in store and additional chemotherapy scheduled, who knows when I would be on the road again? As I ride on Sundays, there is a sense of tranquility and freedom that I don't feel any other time during the week. No schedule. No chores. Nature all around me. I'm always so grateful to be able to do the ride, and I have never taken for granted the inspirational and uplifting experience this has become.

The mood-enhancing result of this outdoor exercise lasts for at least a full day, often extending into the work week. Today, I stopped to take a photo of a group of longhorn steer grazing by the road. I also stopped at the Arbor Hills Nature Preserve, watching families and dogs enjoy the morning. As I reached our neighborhood on the route home, I took an additional short spin through a park, wanting to preserve this sense of tranquility as long as possible. I arrived home shortly after 11:00, to the welcoming smile of Nancy. What better way to begin a day?

Today, I began to experience what I had been told about. I felt a little nauseous as the day wore on. I was given two different prescriptions at the time of my treatment and had them both filled. The nurse explained that patients react differently, and one might be more effective than the other. He also told me not to wait until the nausea became severe. There was no need to be uncomfortable. He told me that once a pattern is established as to the times of my peak symptoms, I should take the anti-nausea medicine in anticipation of the nausea. I took my first dose this evening and will try to ascertain a pattern of the nausea, so I can avoid the worst of the symptom.

Monday, November 10
My appearance has changed.

I decided to approach my patients with news of my illness in a very direct way. They would see my changed appearance and would no doubt have concerns and questions. I prepared a letter that would be given to each patient as they entered the office. I tried to think ahead – not only about my lack of hair, but also the mask that I would be wearing on days 6-12 after my treatment to reduce my risk of infection, and the lack of personal touch with a handshake or a hug. I wanted to make the letter brief and to the point, yet sensitive to what would undoubtedly be their concerns. I instructed my secretary, Michelle, to hand the letter to each patient as they signed in for their appointment. Here is the body of the letter I prepared for them:

To my patients:
You will no doubt notice that my appearance has changed. I'm being treated for lymphoma. There goes the hair (Though it was starting to go even before my treatment!).

If I'm wearing a mask, it is to protect me from all the nasty bugs around. I am not infectious.

If I don't shake hands or give you a hug, please understand that again, it's to protect me because of my compromised immune system.

My mind is working just fine – if it wasn't, I wouldn't be at work today.

So . . . this appointment is about YOU, not ME. If you have a question or two, by all means ask. But then, let's get down to the business at hand – taking care of your health needs. That, after all, is why we're both here.

Thank you for your understanding.

There is no reason for me to wear a hat, and there would be no need for me to hide behind nondescript excuses for my appearance. The letter describes what I'm dealing with. I'm doing what I can to get better. Let's move on. So often, patients have a whole litany of complaints that need to be addressed. I fully understand and accept my role in allaying their fears, making accurate diagnoses and instituting proper treatment. The letter is a way to demonstrate that, while medical conditions are often uncomfortable and emotionally distressing, the best way to deal with them is through a combination of action and composure.

My nausea is somewhat better, and the dizziness is essentially gone. If I didn't look in the mirror, I wouldn't know that my health has changed. While my patients will be concerned about me, my task is to reassure them that all is well with the practice and that they will continue to be cared for.

Tuesday, November 11
"You have a lot of patients who need you to be well."

I can definitely see the value of anticipating when the nausea will hit. This morning (early morning, as in around 4:00 a.m.) I was awakened by nausea. Not severe enough to vomit, but definitely enough to keep me awake. By the time the antinausea medicine began to work, it was almost time to get up and get ready for work. Maybe I should listen to the nurse's advice and take the nausea medicine every night. I dislike the idea of taking medicine for nausea even when I'm not having any symptoms. This will take some time to get used to.

Patients have been so kind today. I suppose it is quite surprising to go the doctor's office and find that the doctor himself is ill. It takes much grace on the part of an individual to put their immediate needs aside for a moment and to address another person with care and feeling. Several patients today expressed their feelings for me and encouraged me. The best way to reciprocate is to get better, so I can continue to care for them.

As predicted, the combination of chemotherapy and stress has taken a toll. Nothing seems to feel the same as it did. I still have my slight equilibrium problem. I don't feel like I might fall, but rather that like my inner "atmospherics" have been changed a lot. I have frequent periods of slight nausea, and this evening had a throbbing sensation in my chest. There is no doubt that this increased awareness of my heartbeat is due to tension. All of this is new. I have indigestion from the prednisone and feel more fatigued than usual as the day wears on.

Nancy again tried to reassure me that the oncology team treats lymphoma all the time, and I just have to trust that they are experts and that things will turn out fine. Intellectually, I realize that this is true, but I've seen too many times when complications arise and a poor course results. Perhaps that's the real source of much of my emotional distress. As my treatments continue, I expect that I will gain confidence. Although I won't necessarily feel any better physically, I will know what to expect.

Wednesday, November 12
"Your white blood cell count is very low."

Today is the one-week mark since my treatment. As per my instructions, I had blood drawn this morning to check my blood count and some of the chemistries in my bloodstream. Dr. Tang called me in the early evening to report the results. Chemotherapy leaves us on a razor's edge. We need to kill all the bad cells, but we are only beginning to have the means to spare the good cells. We're not there yet.

White blood cells are responsible for fighting infection, yet it is a subset of my white blood cells that are the troublemakers – the B-lymphocytes. In the process of knocking these bad guys off, inevitably there is collateral damage to the good guys. And my good guys were small in number – very small! The normal number of infection-fighting granulocytes – a portion of our white blood cells – is between 2,000 and 8,000. My count was 360. I had no idea what to expect the count to be, but Dr. Tang's call indicated he expected it to be higher than this.

Dr. Tang expressed his concern and told me that I might want to check in with my oncology team, since I was at very high risk for infection. The doctor on call for Dr. Naina responded quickly to my phone call, and she was also concerned. She told me to come right to the hospital if I run a fever, and of the proper precautions to take. I was to avoid crowds, have no close contact with anyone, and wear a mask if I go to the office to see patients. She sounded a bit alarmed and told me to check with my doctor's office in the morning. The doctor told me that I was "wide open" for infection. Another restless night of worry was in store.

Once worry sets in, all sorts of sensations take on new and potentially important meaning. The slight and transient scratchy feeling in the back of my throat – am I getting strep? With few white blood cells, will the strep overtake me before I can get help? What should I pay attention to? What should I ignore? Should I go to work tomorrow? What if my white blood cell count falls yet further? There are so many bodily sensations that we accept as normal and overlook. Now, each carries with it potentially ominous implications and could represent a harbinger of serious illness.

Thursday, November 13
"This is about what we typically see."

I made contact with Ariel, the nurse from Dr. Naina's office, shortly after 8:00. Her nonchalance was reassuring. My "five-alarm worry" was reduced to only "two-alarm concern" after our conversation. "Par for the course . . . This is about what we typically see . . . It's okay to work, just wear a mask . . . The next laboratory work, when we check your blood count again, should be drawn in a week . . . No need to have it sooner . . . Come to the hospital if you run a fever."

This is the same message I had been given before and is just another aspect of the new reality I'm living with. While relieved, I was a bit upset. If my lab results were simply par for the course, why had the on-call doctor not known that? I had so much needless anxiety last night. Well, rather than focus on the worry of last night, I will instead focus on the fact that things are going as expected. Nancy again reminded me that the team at the clinic deals with this all the time. I need to try to relax and let them guide me. If they tell me not to worry, then I shouldn't worry.

Actually, this was the first morning since my treatment that I actually felt close to normal. I had no nausea, no heartburn, and a relatively good energy level. For the next week, I am to wear a mask all day. Upon entering my exam rooms, I quickly announced, "Don't worry – the mask is to protect me, not you." Patients had already received my letter when they checked in, and perhaps surprisingly, the visits and my interactions with patients were routine. I didn't make a big deal out of it, and neither did patients. A few asked about my condition, and many expressed their hope that things go well, but the day was otherwise a routine one.

So now there are two distinct changes in my appearance – the short hair and the mask. Still, I try very hard to present a cheerful and friendly attitude upon entering the exam room. Patients usually respond in kind. People react to their surroundings, and their attitude typically reflects how they are treated.

When my ultrasound technologist, Sheli, first began working in my office she commented about how nice our patients were. I responded that people were people. Our patients are no different from those in other practices. But when a patient is met at the check-in counter with a friendly welcome by Michelle, when my nurse Gayle treats them with caring and kindness, and when they are greeted for their ultrasound study by Sheli's smile and her friendly manner, people will typically respond with a similar demeanor – a friendly smile and a pleasant disposition. There are always exceptions, of course, but when most people are treated with good cheer and kindness, they respond in a positive way.

Friday, November 14
Another medical issue.

I have had ringing in my ear for several months. It is in my left ear, in which I had known hearing loss since early childhood – possibly a congenital condition or the result of the mumps virus, which infected me early in first grade. This sensation was different, though – a continual high-pitched sound that was very annoying. I hadn't gone to an ear doctor prior to today because of the lymphoma, but had made this appointment a couple of weeks ago and wanted to keep it.

Most of the time, the ringing ("tinnitus") is simply the result of aging and associated hearing loss, but there can be more dangerous causes, and I really needed to get it checked out. The hearing test showed pretty much what I expected – some loss of hearing in my right ear, consistent with a patient in my age group, and a much more severe loss of hearing in the left ear.

The ear, nose and throat specialist, Dr. Kapadia, reviewed the results with me. The tinnitus was likely with me to stay and was, as in most cases, simply associated with hearing loss and age. The more serious causes of tinnitus would have to be eliminated with an MRI scan, and Dr. Kapadia suggested that I speak with Dr. Naina about the best time to have this done. We don't want to interfere with my chemotherapy, and the MRI was not emergent.

For the tinnitus, I could try a type of hearing aid that emits its own noise-cancelling sound, but I should expect that even this would only be partially effective. My hearing would, of course, improve with the hearing aid, but that is a separate issue. I can work in my office an entire day without asking someone to repeat him or herself, so my hearing loss is not a major problem. Although I'm not opposed to wearing a hearing aid and most likely will need one even for normal discourse, the main reason I went to the doctor – the tinnitus – will most likely be a chronic condition. Yet another reminder of the march of time and its unavoidable effects.

As people age, the body inevitably sends off unwelcome signals. Aches here, pains there and assorted new and unwelcome sensations. Most of these symptoms do not reflect serious illness. I jokingly call this, "calendar disease." Many patients become somewhat despondent about the aging process and the increasing number of ailments they have. When patients express sadness over these unwanted conditions, I tell them that the body is simply a mechanical device for carrying around their soul. Their very essence – their mind and personality – are separate, and are what make them unique. In Hebrew, we call this essence the *neshama* (soul), which makes us who we are.

We may not be able to do much about the mechanical breakdowns that occur in our bodies, but we can and must appreciate what makes us unique and loved – our *neshama*. So we need to have equanimity about the aging process, while doing our best to continue to let the best of our personalities shine through.

Increasingly, I will be put to that test. I will try my best to follow my own advice to patients. Tinnitus? I can live with it and will do so without becoming grumpy. Loss of hearing? When the time comes, I will get a hearing aid. Lymphoma? I will be grateful that there is chemotherapy that gives me a chance to live. I will keep my chin up, and will do what I need to do every day.

Saturday, November 15
Sealed envelopes.

I have completed a difficult but necessary assignment. I have written letters to the most important people in my life, as well as a letter in which I spelled out my final wishes. The letters will be safeguarded by a close friend and distributed if I die. The call to my friend was a difficult one to make, but he fully grasped the importance the letters had to me, and told me he was honored to have been asked to carry out this task. My intention is to update the letters periodically.

I actually wrote these letters one time before, when my Crohn's Disease was very severe in 2006 and there did not seem to be effective treatment. Now, years later, the letters needed to be updated. Although I was quite emotional as I composed these messages, I felt a great sense of calm and relief once they were finished.

There is a tradition in Judaism that goes back to Biblical times of imparting final messages to loved ones near the time of death. My letters are not long discourses of lessons learned throughout my life. Rather, they are personal messages that I want to be sure are transmitted when the time comes. Hopefully, the envelopes will not need to be opened for many years, but we can never know for certain when the day will come.

Sunday, November 16
The still, small voice.

At our synagogue's weekly Shabbat service on Saturday morning, one of our members presents a *D'var Torah* – a teaching, based on the weekly Torah portion. Literally, the Hebrew term *D'var Torah* means "Words of Torah." It is used to refer to a teaching, often in a group setting. A *D'var Torah* can be delivered as part of a worship service or to begin a meeting of a Jewish organization or group. The basis of the teaching is the Torah, the written laws of Judaism, passed on from generation to generation, beginning with Moses. It can also draw from the Talmud, the oral law that explains and expounds on much of what is contained in the Torah. Additionally, the teaching can be derived from the writings of the Prophets or other similar Hebrew sources.

I will be offering the teaching in two weeks, which will be the Saturday after Thanksgiving. My chemotherapy is scheduled for the prior Wednesday, so I'm hopeful I won't be too nauseous that morning. Preparing the *D'var Torah* is enjoyable and challenging. The right mix of information and inspiration, sprinkled with just a bit of humor and maybe a personal anecdote are essential for keeping a congregation's attention. Preparing this talk keeps me focused on doing positive things rather than thinking about my medical situation and the various ill effects I experience from the medications.

Studying for and writing a *D'var Torah* is medication in a different sense – it restores and heals the soul, allowing me to energetically delve into a project that will benefit others. This type of "spiritual drug" supplements more traditional forms of remedies.

In two weeks, the Torah portion is about Jacob, in which he flees his family and has a mysterious dream. It is the beginning of his spiritual awakening and consequently marks the beginning of his transformation as a person. I have already written much of my talk, and today awoke (much too early!) with the thought of an addition that I feel will make the story more personal to the listeners. To what I have already written, I will add the story of the prophet Elijah, and how he heard a "Still, small voice." The thought didn't come out of the blue – I had thought about such an addition to the *D'var Torah* yesterday, but only now, as I lay in bed, did the final form take shape. I worked on it during the morning, and here is a portion:

Our concepts of God are certainly diverse and are often conflicted. Emet V'Emunah *is the statement of principles of Conservative Judaism written by, among others, the United Synagogue and the Jewish Theological Seminary. In this work, we read, "God is a source of great perplexity and confusion . . . Doubts and uncertainties are inevitable . . ."*

Perplexity, confusion, doubt, uncertainty. Four words that you won't find in many other faiths. The statement goes on, "One can live fully and authentically as a Jew without having a single satisfactory answer to such doubts; one cannot, however, live a thoughtful Jewish life without having asked the questions."

God appears at various times in the Hebrew Bible, but one that resonates with me and that is stated beautifully involved the prophet Elijah.

Elijah lived during the time of the corrupt King Ahab and his non-Jewish and also corrupt queen, Jezebel. Elijah prophesized the end of their sinful reign, and the end of all the idolatry that surrounded them. He then fled the enraged monarchs, escaping into the desert. He cried out to God, complaining about what he had seen and what he had experienced. He wanted an answer and an end to all this sin.

You may remember the well-known segment. Elijah

*received a response. There was an earthquake, but God was not in the earthquake; there was a great wind, but God was not in the wind; there was a fire, but God was not in the fire. Then, it was perfectly quiet in the desert . . . and Elijah heard a still, small voice. "Who are you, really, Elijah? Why are you here?" Elijah heard the voice and the question as a direct message from God. Instead of sympathizing with Elijah, God gave him instructions as to what he must do in order to help eliminate the sinful behavior he had witnessed, and sent him on his way. In other words, God told Elijah, "Don't just complain. **Do** something about it!"*

The Jacob narrative during these weeks holds out promise that any life can be changed. Ennobled. Elevated. God is found not only at the end of the journey. Our lives' journeys, after all, usually have no end. Rather, God is found in the steps we take along the way, especially the painful and transformative steps. As God told Jacob during his journey, "Remember, my child, I am not done with you."

Every time we hear the Shm'a *prayer, we should hear it not only as a call to Israel as a nation, but also to each of us personally. We should try to hear what Jacob heard and what Elijah heard. It was the call to be a force for good and for healing in the world.*

"Here is what you need to do," says the still, small voice. "I will be with you."

Our task is clear. As a parent, child, friend, Jew, and in all our other capacities, our job is to bring God to earth, and into our lives. To hear and feel what holiness is.

Amidst the struggles and the everyday worries, and in all our life journeys, we can find holiness as defined in the great teachings of Judaism. A holiness defined by helping and caring for others and by peacefully healing the world.

So even with all our perplexity, confusion, doubt and uncertainty, God can still be in our lives. As with Jacob and as with Elijah, we just have to know where to look, and we just have to know how to listen.

The past month or so has been an emotionally fraught time for me. The *D'var Torah* has given me ample opportunity to find renewed meaning in the teachings of our ancestors.

Monday, November 17
"It could be worse."

I had a call last night from a friend from out of town. I realize that the call was meant to express care and concern, but it was actually quite annoying. In discussing my battle with cancer, the friend told me how much worse this actually could be. He mentioned a type of blood disorder that was more lethal than mine. I frequently hear of other such examples, where well-meaning people tell someone who is ill or who has had some other untoward fate befall them – an accident, for instance – how lucky they were. "Think of how much worse this actually could have been!"

Well, people who are ill, people who have fallen and suffered a serious injury, or those who have been in a car accident and suffered trauma don't feel especially lucky. They certainly shouldn't have to hear that things could have been worse. After all, there are practically no situations that could not be worse! When I hear that things could be *worse*, my immediate reaction is that things could also be a whole lot *better* – the illness or injury might not have happened at all. Wouldn't that be much better? It is of no comfort for people in distress to hear how fortunate they are that their situation is not worse. How insensitive!

Although different from my case, the same situation occurs when a person of advanced years dies. The spouse or child is sometimes told how lucky they are to have had a long relationship with the deceased. At that particular time, the grieving relative typically doesn't feel fortunate. A loss is still a loss. We can look at the situation from afar and think, "They were married for 50 years. How fortunate they were. What a long time!" But for the spouse who is left alone, the loss of a spouse is not a period of rejoicing.

On the physical front, I have had a normal energy level for several days. Perhaps things will be different as I go through each three-week interval, but I had been told that the second week after treatment would be marked by weakness, as the effects of the chemotherapy would not be mitigated by the buoyant effect of prednisone, and that as the effect of prednisone wears off after its five-day course, I would feel gradually weaker. So far, so good. My emotional distress is lifting, and I can feel myself regaining my physical strength as well.

Wednesday, November 19
The Mormons are on board!

I've had many patients tell me that they have been praying for me. So far, patients and friends from several religions and denominations have told me that I'm on their prayer list at church, or that I am in their personal prayers – Presbyterians, Baptists, and today a Mormon. And it has only been a couple of weeks since people have known! It seems as though I'm well covered.

Although I've never been one to believe that God can be petitioned, I'm very grateful that someone would think enough of me to pray for my good health. It doesn't matter to me that I really don't believe that "intercessionary" prayer (This is a term often used when praying for the healing of someone who is ill.) has a tangible effect. It tells me that people care. Although my spirits are high and I have a confident attitude about my eventual recovery, the knowledge that people care about me gives me comfort and even more determination to recover.

I recall a time some years ago when I was hospitalized in Richardson. The hospital chaplain came to my bedside and offered a prayer on my behalf. He knew I was Jewish because I had given a talk to the hospital chaplains about previous writings I had done. He closed his eyes, said how much I meant to the people of the community, and asked God for my recovery. It was very warm and comforting. The hospital chaplain's prayer struck the perfect chord and stayed in my mind long after I recovered.

Thursday, November 20
"Plenty of white blood cells."

D r. Tang called me early this morning. I can take off the mask! My white cell count is robust, close to 7,000. The key component of the white cells – the leukocytes – is now normal, with a count of almost 6,000. My army of blood cells has plenty of infection-fighting soldiers. There has been a rapid recovery of my white blood cell count as anticipated by my oncology team. For the next week or so, I will not be required to hide behind a protective mask.

This afternoon, Rabbi Gershon texted me, and asked how I was doing. I texted back that I felt strong, and that Nancy calls me a "badass!" The thought of my rabbi reading this text brought a smile to me the rest of the day.

I also received a telephone call from our Cantor, Yitzhak Zhrebker. He was calling from his car. The voice quality was grainy, and at one point, he asked me to wait just a minute. I heard him yelling, "You lost your load! You lost your load!" He explained that he had just passed a truck that lost a load of material. It apparently had slid off the back of the vehicle. The cantor had pulled up alongside the truck and was trying to tell the driver what had happened.

The image of this kind and gentle bearded man with a heavy Russian accent yelling to a trucker was so amusing, I could imagine a television skit built around the scene. It has cast an enduring image in my mind. I quickly mentioned to him that maybe he shouldn't be on the phone at that particular time, though I really appreciated his call.

Friday, November 21
The three-week interval between treatments.

This was a good week. I have felt strong, and am better emotionally. With the plunge in my white blood cell count and the continued low lymphocyte count, I am confident that the chemotherapy is doing what it is supposed to do. Certainly, when I receive my treatment next week, I will be in a better state – both physically and emotionally – than I was for my first treatment.

My concept of the three-week intervals between treatments is that the first week is marked by nausea and other side effects from the drugs. The second week is marked by low blood counts and the generalized weakness that comes with the discontinuation of prednisone from the regimen. The third week is for recovery before the next round. During that week, patients should begin to regain their strength from the prior treatment.

Fortunately, I did not have a marked "low" period when I stopped the prednisone, and didn't feel weak from the low blood count. So I will have had almost two good weeks. I hope this gives me a better chance of not having the predicted severe and progressive weakness with future treatments, though Shawn, the nurse who attended my first treatment, told me that patients often get progressively weaker with ensuing treatments. I hope to minimize that slide and downward spiral. This may just be wishful thinking, but I hope it is grounded in at least some data, based on how I feel this week.

Sunday, November 23
Just an abnormal cell line.

I went on a bike ride today and was joined for part of the ride by two friends from my shul, Ron Steiner and Guy Bradley. I rode fifty-one miles, and I felt great. (Well, actually, my legs were understandably quite tired by the time I finished.)

During a phone call with my brother this afternoon, I told him of my ride, and he was incredulous at its length. "Are you sure you're sick?" he asked. "I'm not sick, Mark," I responded. "I just have an abnormal cell line in my body that unfortunately requires strong medicine to eradicate." After I responded in that way, I decided that was a good way to think of my condition. I am not sick – I just need medicine to clean out some unwanted cells from my body.

Prior to today, my last bike ride was a couple of days after my first chemotherapy treatment. My mindset is so much better today. Before beginning treatment, I knew that there were cancer cells streaming through my bone marrow, and had not yet begun receiving any medicine to eradicate them. I was worried about my condition and somewhat fearful of the treatment. Today was different – I'm now essentially through with the first three-week cycle and feel none the worse for wear. I am doing something positive to attack the malignant cells. I had a few days with nausea and a scare from a very low white blood cell count, but I have been strong since, and I am ready and willing to get after more of those abnormal lymphocytes.

Monday, November 24

"Not on a Friday. The beneficial effects of volunteerism, optimism and spirituality."

M r. Johnson is now over 90 years old. I first met him in 1981, when he had a heart attack. Through the years, he has maintained an unfailingly positive attitude. He has a close relationship with his extended family, and he still volunteers in a food pantry. When I finish my examination and office visit and my secretary is about to schedule his next visit, he is quick to remind her that he volunteers on Fridays, so his appointments must be on another day. Certainly, there is some good fortune involved in his longevity. One doesn't live into the tenth decade of life without it. But could there be something more?

Stephen Krause from the University of Michigan published a study – one of several such studies with similar conclusions – in which those in faith communities who were involved in volunteer activities had a better medical prognosis than those who were not involved with such activities. A book written by Stephen Post, *Why Good Things Happen to Good People*, demonstrates and explains how helping others reduces stress and anxiety, and facilitates other beneficial changes in one's health. Might Mr. Johnson have benefitted from his volunteerism?

In addition to explaining the effects of volunteerism on health, there is a body of medical literature studying the "mind-body connection." After accounting for a variety of medical variables, a study on the benefits of optimism published in the *Archives of Internal Medicine* in 2006 demonstrated that those with an optimistic outlook on life have a better medical prognosis than those who don't.

From the time I first met him, Mr. Johnson's attitude was, "Okay, so I have this condition. I'll take care of it. Now, let me get back to what I do!" He has always shown optimism about the future, and exemplified that attitude by the way he has lived his life.

Assuming the conclusions from all these studies are justified, the answer of why there is such a strong correlation between volunteerism and an optimistic attitude with a better medical prognosis is speculative. By its very nature, volunteerism involves some form of connectedness with others, and to a large degree, volunteers have a purpose – a mission – in life that extends beyond themselves.

This connectedness and sense of mission might also tie into the correlation between a sense of spirituality and generally better health. Of course, there are exceptions to this. Certainly not all who volunteer or who are spiritual or who enjoy time with friends are healthy. But as a group, the trend is in that direction.

The literature is very consistent, and I intend to take full advantage of whatever benefit these traits confer. I cannot leave my intellect at the door – I fully understand the limitations and possible complications of my treatment as well as the gravity of having Stage 4 lymphoma, but I can still visualize a good outcome from my condition. Part of that visualization involves my own actions, my involvement with others, and how those actions and connections can help bring about a positive outcome. I am working toward that result.

Beyond the improved medical prognosis imparted by these activities and this mindset, there is the important "quality of life" parameter to consider. Having something to live for – living life with a purpose – is a very powerful force. For some people it means seeing friends. For others, it means enjoying and maybe in some way helping family members. For still others, it can involve work or volunteer activities. But a sense of mission can serve as a motivating stimulus for everyone. After all, we are all here for but a short time. How we use that time is far more important than how many days we live.

Wednesday, November 26
Second treatment.

After arriving at the cancer treatment center, I was promptly taken back to the infusion area. Although the quality of care is top-notch, this part of the hospital needs renovation. The main infusion area is a room with six reclining chairs. The area is a bit crowded, and the room is fully open to the main corridor of the cancer treatment area, so patients, nurses and assorted others are continually marching past. The combination of conversations, doors opening and closing, and alarms from the infusion machine did not produce a very relaxing environment. I must remember to bring earplugs next time. There are some smaller infusion rooms, and it occurred to me that if I am placed in this room next time, maybe I can request one of the smaller rooms. It's worth a try.

My book bag was packed with journals, newspaper sections from the previous couple of days, magazines, the DVD player that Leah had given me, my iPod and iPad, and snacks. I always bring more than I will have time to get through, but at least I have a choice of what to occupy my time with. This is almost like a long airplane flight for me. As long as I'm not too uncomfortable, I have lots of time with absolutely no scheduled activities. It sounds strange, but there is a saving grace in going through the infusion – I have lots of time to catch up on whatever I want to do.

In the midst of the treatment I was taken to an exam room for my appointment with Dr. Naina. He was generally happy with how things seemed to be going and expressed confidence that we would have a good result. He did not feel that any changes were needed in the protocol of medicines being used. The nausea is as expected. The medicine I am taking for this is doing a pretty good job, and anything stronger would make me sleepy, so we will continue as is. He explained that I should not worry about the low white blood cell count. In fact, now that he knows what the low point is for my white blood cells, at least for now there would be no need for further blood work between treatments.

Precautions were needed, though, to protect me from infection. From day 6 after treatment until day 12, I should wear a mask when seeing patients or having any close encounters with anyone. I should avoid crowds during this time, so shopping malls, groups of friends and restaurants are basically off limits during this time frame.

A PET scan will be scheduled early on the morning of my next treatment, so we can see how much progress we are making. That will give Dr. Naina an indication of whether we are on the right track or whether any changes in the regimen are needed.

During the infusion, there were many messages from friends by email, and I missed a call from my friend, Rabbi David Glickman, during the afternoon. I was bothered again by nausea and had generalized weakness when I got home, but a tablet of my anti-nausea medication did the trick. Dinner with Nancy cheered me, as it always does. Despite having a very sedentary day, I was very tired all evening, and went to sleep earlier than usual.

Thursday, November 27
Thanksgiving.

Thanksgiving is at or near the top of almost everyone's list of favorite holidays. There is no agenda, no specific event to celebrate, no religious observance. Because it is celebrated on Thursday, Friday is also a day off from work for most, so there is a four-day break from the usual routine. Mark and Ina joined us for the holiday, and Leah has traveled from New York. We will also have a few others at our home for dinner. My good friend Sarita and her daughter Zoey will also be with us. Sarita has been a long-time friend, and she has called frequently during the last few weeks.

On Thanksgiving, as well as other days, we must always be appreciative for what we have and not take our blessings for granted. Although we are always with family and friends on Thanksgiving, this one has special meaning. Although there were no "pearls of wisdom" that anyone had for me, it was very special just being able to spend time with those closest to me. Their presence alone lifted my spirits greatly.

A story:
A fire enveloped a house quickly as the family prepared for the children's bedtime. As the family gathered on the sidewalk, a panicked father asked God for help – his child was still inside! "Please God, let my child be saved!" Just then, a firefighter came running out from the house carrying the child. The father embraced his child, and again addressed God, but was a bit annoyed. "As I recall, he was wearing slippers."

Many people have a habit of never being fully satisfied. I may not have my "slippers" today, but I do have much to be thankful about. I never take my family or my many other blessings for granted. In the blink of an eye things change, so we must always give thanks and express in words and deed our gratitude for what we have.

Saturday, November 29
My synagogue presentation.

I still tend to resist taking my anti-nausea pill before bed, and again paid the price. I dislike taking medicine for a symptom I don't have. But last night, I was awakened again in the wee hours of the morning with nausea. After taking the pill, though, the nausea abated, and I was able to get back to sleep. Just as after the first treatment, I can feel the effects of the drugs in these first couple of days, as they are working their way into the tissues and cells of the body. I can definitely tell that something is in my system that doesn't belong there.

Mark and I went to shul together this morning; the rest of the family joined us a bit later. As I sat there with Mark, I thought of how proud our parents would be to see the two of us in a close relationship, side-by-side in shul.

Shabbat services were well attended, and I delivered the *D'var Torah* that I wrote about on November 16. As I hoped, it was well received. Normally, as I am speaking, I scan the room. Typically, several people are dozing. (This is not unusual. Other speakers would find the same thing!) This time, though, virtually all eyes were on me continually. I could tell that the talk resonated and had meaning among many of the congregants. I wonder if the topic seemed especially relevant to the congregants because of what I was going through with my health. It was my first foray into the realm of a personal theology of sorts, and several people asked if I would send them the talk electronically.

Mark seemed especially moved by the talk. I could tell even after I finished that he was thinking about the "still, small voice" that I had discussed.

Not unexpectedly, I had no symptoms at all during the talk. I find that when I am deeply engaged in an activity, I have few if any symptoms. Many people find this to be true, no matter what their malady is. Distraction is thus a good reason for patients to remain involved in whatever might be of interest.

Sunday, November 30
Is there an issue with my biking drink mix?

Today was very windy. Ron joined me after my usual 15-mile route to the Arbor Hills Nature Preserve, but my legs felt more tired than usual. I took a couple of swigs from my drink mix and it seemed to have very little flavor. I couldn't decide whether I had forgotten to add a second scoop of the mix, or whether the bottle simply hadn't been shaken up properly, since it was refrigerated overnight. Eventually, when even my electrolyte jellies had little flavor, I realized that the issue involved my taste buds, not the drink mix! In fact, nothing I put in my mouth had much flavor. My taste buds are taking a vacation. This also happened after my first treatment, and lasted several days. Hopefully, it will again be limited in time. In fact, it occurred to me while I was riding that even the characteristic tingle in my mouth when rinsing with my mouthwash was gone!

As the ride continued, Ron and I had nice banter – a very enjoyable ride – but my legs never felt as strong as they typically do. The hills seemed steeper than usual. I even checked my tires to see if they were flat, but they were inflated properly. Every rotation of the pedals seemed to be a struggle, and I curtailed my ride to 40 miles. Certainly, this is still a long ride, but I definitely did not feel as strong as I normally do. I made it home without any difficulty, but given the calendar and the colder weather ahead, and because I will be off the bike next week when my white blood cell count will be very low, I again realize that it may be some weeks or even months before I can ride my bicycle outdoors again.

Nancy and I went to see her mother this afternoon. She has severe Alzheimer's Disease and is losing ground weekly. Nancy has been very devoted to her, and has ensured that she has been kept comfortable and dignified, but the progression of the disease is relentless. With her declining level of consciousness, her life expectancy is short. It's so sad to see her in this condition. This is not how I want to remember her.

Monday, December 1
My dad's birthday.

My father died when he was thirty-eight years old. He sustained a knee injury at work, and 1959 was long before arthroscopy and the relatively simple repairs on torn knee cartilage that we are able to do now. He was put to bed for a couple of weeks, and the doctor's plan was to do surgery if he did not improve. Instead, his immobility led to a blood clot that traveled to his lungs and caused his death.

At the time, I was eight years old and my brother was fourteen. We lived in a third-floor apartment in the Dorchester section of Boston. Dad worked as a dispatcher for a trucking company during the week and drove a taxicab on weekends. After he died, our family was observing our week of mourning – seven days in the Jewish religion. This week is called *shiva* (Hebrew for seven).

One day during that week, we answered our doorbell, and up the stairs to our apartment walked a Catholic priest with a bouquet of flowers. He told my mother that if the weather was inclement on a Sunday morning, dad would pick the priest up at the rectory and drive him in his taxi the couple of blocks to his church. The priest told us that my dad never took a dime from him.

I remember playing with my father and have only good memories of him. After he died, I recall mailing some letters for my mother in a mailbox down the street. An older man who was our neighbor approached me at the mailbox and, trying to console me, said, "You have to understand, Joel, that God *needs* your father." Although I was only eight years old at the time, I distinctly recall what I thought, though I can't remember if I said it out loud to this well-meaning neighbor: "But *I* need my father!" It seems that my issues with the concept of Divine intervention go back a long way. I was echoing a theme that has been a source of much discussion and of many books. Why indeed did such a bad thing happen to such a good man and such a close-knit family?

Tomorrow is day 6 after my treatment. Recalling Dr. Naina's recommendation at our last visit, beginning tomorrow, I will again be the "Masked Marvel" at work for the next week. Compared with the way I felt the first few days after my first treatment, I am stronger and in better spirits. There is no doubt that some of this comes from knowing what to expect and settling into a regular pattern. Unfortunately, my taste buds are still on vacation. The infusion nurse told me that this might be an ongoing problem for the duration of my chemotherapy.

Wednesday, December 3
Ritual observance.

B ill Gershon, the senior rabbi of Congregation Shearith Israel in Dallas, came to the office yesterday. Nancy and I have been members of this synagogue since 1985, and Nancy is now the incoming President of the shul's sisterhood – a very big job. The rabbi's visit was a very nice gesture of concern. We didn't get into a spiritual discussion, but I'm sure he would have been willing to if I so chose. I'm not looking for "answers," though. Coming the day after my father's birthday, and given what I am dealing with, I am reminded of some explanations of theodicy – attempts to reconcile the coexistence of suffering and of God.

I understand that many will not view God in the same way, but I don't believe that bad things happen as Divine punishment, and I don't believe there is a Divine lesson that I'm supposed to learn from my illness. It's simply not tenable for me to believe that God is micromanaging the world, directly causing every event to transpire just the way God wants it to. I cannot and do not believe in a God that would directly cause either natural disasters in which thousands of people die, or events such as the Holocaust in which millions are killed.

In his book, *God Was Not in the Fire*, Daniel Gordis writes that although numerous Jewish philosophers have explored the issue of why evil and suffering exist in the world, "None of those explanations became the authoritative Jewish stance on this complicated subject . . . Judaism does not have one authoritative answer. Judaism's strength lies precisely in the fact that our tradition does not look for a single answer."

In the end, there are at once numerous explanations and no explanations of why bad things happen, seemingly in a random way. The Torah, the Talmud and the Book of

Job all give us the same message: we will never be able to understand why evil and suffering exists. Neil Gillman's book, *Sacred Fragments*, has an in-depth discussion of this topic. Certainly, there are many other such sources. It is a subject that has been discussed by an abundance of theologians, rabbis and philosophers.

Far be it for me to break new ground on this topic. Having no personally satisfying answer despite studying a number of Jewish sources, I have found that my only task when faced with adversity is to deal with it. However illness or other misfortune may have come about, my only task is to confront the question, "What next? How am I going to cope? How shall I respond?"

Part of that response revolves around the fact that I have found comfort in many of the rituals of Judaism. Although I'm not observant of all Jewish laws and customs, many have provided an anchor for me – a scaffold upon which I find joy, comfort and connection. The connection seems to extend both horizontally – to friends and family, and vertically – to others who have come before me and to those who will come after me. The apparent chaos of life is thus countered by instances and examples of structure.

Last summer, I presented a *D'var Torah* on *Parasha Ekev* (a *parasha* is a specific portion of the Torah. This particular one is named *Ekev* – Hebrew for "as a consequence of") in which we read of tangible rewards for following the commandments in the Torah, and curses if we do not. My teaching discussed the importance and values of ritual, even in the face of the disconnect between religious observance and tangible reward. Here is an excerpt:

Agudath Israel was the name of the orthodox shul I attended as a small child in Boston. Mr. Kaufman was my very first Hebrew school teacher in elementary school. He was very stern. Rumor had it that someone saw him actually smile on one occasion, but it was never confirmed.

The bedtime prayer – Shm'a, I was taught, had to be recited absolutely perfectly. On many a night my sleep was delayed for a long time until I was able to recite the Shm'a without any errors. I would repeat it until it was just right. Living in Mr. Kaufman's world, who knew what horrible fate awaited me if I strayed from the perfect recitation of the Shm'a? I was taking no chances.

In today's parasha, we read a section from Deuteronomy that includes part of the Shm'a. The Israelites are told of rewards to come if they follow God's commandments and punishments if they do not. There is no ambiguity here.

When I was 8 years old, my very kind and loving father died. He had a knee injury, and in 1959, in the days before arthroscopy, his knee was immobilized for three weeks. He developed a blood clot that went to his lungs, and he died.

I realized at a very young age how silly the concept was that being good leads to rewards in life. That was just the beginning of why I have such a problem with interpreting today's parasha, Ekev.

I had such a difficult time with this parasha that I read lessons from it in a number of sources. The discussions covered various aspects of the Torah portion, including the definition of God's greatness, what true power is, and on and on. Maybe I stopped looking too soon, but I couldn't find even <u>one</u> that discussed the elephant in the room: the overt teachings of the parasha are inconsistent with what we know to be true! And yet we read it as part of our liturgy every day. We surely know that keeping God's commandments is not necessarily rewarded in any tangible way. We also know that evil people sometimes live very prosperous and otherwise very happy lives.

Over and over again, the parasha repeats the demand that the Israelites should revere God and keep God's commandments, and that they would reap tangible rewards.

Just as we implore toddlers to do certain things for tangible rewards, that's what today's parasha promises the Israelites. Actually, given that the Israelites were in their "toddlerhood," as it were, as a people, today's parasha makes sense. Maybe that's how they had to be taught. But surely we as a people have moved beyond that.

Further, in harsh tones, Moses tells the Israelites that their triumph in conquering the Promised Land will not be because of their good attributes. They are repeatedly told that they are stubborn, wicked and sinful. And even while they are commanded to treat strangers kindly, they are also told to destroy everyone and everything in their way while conquering the Promised Land. How do we reconcile that? No, this is not my favorite parasha. So, where am I with all of the rules and commandments of our people?

*I would argue that to do good deeds and perform mitzvot so that we will garner some unspecified reward, as this parasha promises, **negates the concept of mitzvot as a manifestation of goodness or love of God**. If we do something for a reward, it's purely transactional. "I'll do this so I can get that." It's no different from working for a paycheck. Inherently, it's neither good nor holy. At work, we do some task and we get paid. In this case, if we are halachically observant we are rewarded by God in some way. There is no inherent goodness there. In a similar way, other religions teach that good deeds and proper faith will earn the faithful a place in heaven. So – does the performance of good deeds in those cases merit praise? Not really – essentially, this is bribery.*

And how do we then explain suffering of the righteous and halachically pure? Rabbi Benjamin Blech, an orthodox rabbi, is one of many who have written books that exemplify how you can tie yourself in knots while trying to explain why bad things happen even to good people. Was my dad, for instance, paying the ultimate price for sins that had been unknown to others? Was he paying that price for the sins of his ancestors? Was he dealt an early death so he would be rewarded in the "World to Come?" Was his death actually a blessing masquerading as a curse? Were the Jews of Europe during World War II such sinners that 6 million of them deserved to be killed? Please . . .

We as a people are now <u>past</u> the toddler stage, where we perform ritual mitzvot or acts of loving kindness to others so that we can be rewarded. We now know that it will not necessarily be so. With toddlers, the hope is that they eventually internalize the values we try to impart, without promises of rewards and without threats. Sure enough, as the "toddlerhood" of the Israelite nation grew to maturity, the words of Pirkei Avot, 4:19, were written and ring only too true to us: "It is not in our power to understand the suffering of the righteous or the tranquility of the wicked." So – what to make of all the arcane rules and traditions of our people? Why observe them?

Abraham Joshua Heschel in his book, God in Search of Man, writes, "To reduce Judaism to law, to Halacha, is to dim its light, to pervert its essence, to kill its spirit." On the other hand, he states that reducing it to inwardness, to aggadah – spirit, to basically nothing <u>beyond</u> being a good person, is to ". . . Dissolve its essence and to destroy its reality."

Gemilut Hasadim, acts of loving kindness that go beyond simple ritual and help repair the world are, almost by definition, acts that are <u>not</u> done for tangible reward. For these, we know from our own personal experiences that goodness must be its own reward. Indeed, it is said that the reward for doing a mitzvah is the opportunity to do another mitzvah.

But what about the rituals – acts – that <u>don't</u> help others in an immediate way? Rituals such as keeping kosher or lighting the Sabbath lights.

Rabbi Neil Gillman wrote about ritual in his classic book,

Sacred Fragments. *He discusses how rituals remind us of the ideals of our peoplehood and bind us together. They bind us one to another and from one generation to the next, providing a context through which other acts follow. Think about the rituals of lighting the Shabbat candles and blessing our children, the tradition this represents, and our tranquil and happy mindset afterwards. Consider how we might become a bit emotional when we remember the rituals performed by those family members of generations past.*

It could take an entire talk by itself, but in social psychology, it is well understood that what you do, you will become. So ritual can <u>create</u> *feelings.*

We therefore must <u>allow</u> *our system of mitzvot and rituals create* **in us** <u>*caring, grateful, rooted*</u> *people who help the world become a better place.*

To me, explanations of Divine reward and punishment are simplistic and are not tenable. Explaining undeserved tragedy as a direct manifestation of God's actions works for some, but to me it is almost a desecration of God's name. No, my cancer is simply the result of nature as created by God, and sometimes unpleasant or harmful events occur in nature. My task now is to use my strengths and take advantage of the wonders of science and medicine to recover.

What about ritual? If I don't believe that there is a direct path from the observance of the commandments as set out in the Torah to tangible rewards, why do I bother going to shul? Why avoid nonkosher meats and fish?

Maybe in a world in which such randomness occurs, rituals anchor me – they give me structure and a strong sense of connectedness to others. Attending shul enables me to build friendships based on common values and a common past. Seeing friends at the kosher section of the grocery store imparts a sense of connectedness too often missing in today's world. As I said in the *D'var Torah*, rituals not only reflect beliefs and feelings, they help create them.

In his book, *A Living Covenant*, David Hartman writes, "The human being is not only a fact-seeking animal, but equally and possibly more so, a value-hungry individual seeking direction and significance in life. We hunger for a frame of reference that orders and orients everyday existence into some meaningful pattern. In spite of the extreme importance of facts, their range does not exhaust the sources from which one constructs a *vision of life* that gives meaning and direction to existence." So there. My "vision of life" goes beyond facts, as the following of customs and the performance of ritual surely does.

The past couple of days have been filled with introspection.

On the health front, my workout last night was shorter and less intense than is usual for me. I have a constant feeling of "unwellness," with mild abdominal discomfort and nausea, and generalized weakness. After the first treatment, these symptoms began to lift after five or six days. I'm hoping for the same timeframe, so I can get back to feeling better within the next day or two.

Thursday, December 4
"It makes you appreciate . . ."

When people are placed in uncomfortable situations, they often may speak in platitudes. When facing a sick person, one such platitude is, "It makes you appreciate being well." Some patients have said this to me, and I understand their discomfort upon seeing the way I appear. But I don't feel I need to have lymphoma in order to appreciate better health. Not only do I appreciate it when I feel fine, there is not a single event I participate in without feeling gratitude.

When I go on my outdoor bike ride on Sunday mornings, I feel incredibly fortunate to be able to engage in that particular activity. In fact, when Nancy and I talk about upcoming events, I typically say, "We should all be well," knowing what a narrow bridge we all walk in life. So no, going through treatment for cancer doesn't make me appreciate feeling good.

In Judaism, we are taught to say a prayer and a blessing for a multitude of things, such as having food to eat and for awakening in the morning. There is even a blessing to say when seeing a rainbow! Our religious services begin with a listing of many of the things for which we should give thanks. In fact, the Talmud teaches that one should say 100 blessings a day. Feeling and expressing gratitude places our everyday hardships in context. Although these hardships don't disappear, our mindset is favorably altered when we are able to be thankful for the blessings in our lives.

For some people, the greatest tragedy in life is not in the sorrows that inevitably befall everyone. For those folks, the biggest tragedy is not realizing all for which they should be grateful.

I imagine my life's blessings being like milk. A few drops of milk added to a glass of water change the color of the entire glass. Similarly, a few good drops of life – a few blessings – can change the complexion of an otherwise gloomy day. A day that could be filled with despair and discomfort is modified by things about which I am grateful. Awakening next to my beloved Nancy, for instance – what could be sweeter than that?

This week, I have been called by several friends. The calls are another reminder to me that people care. Even a short call with an expression of concern lifts my spirits greatly. Some people shy away from reaching out to someone who is ill or who has suffered loss. If the person doesn't wish to be engaged, it quickly becomes apparent in the conversation, which can then be curtailed. Most people, though, appreciate the thought and the effort.

Friday, December 5
"I hear you're not working now ..."

I received an email from one of my colleagues:

Hi Joel –
I have heard from a few of my patients that you are not working now due to health issues. I hope this is only temporary and you will be back to normal soon! I am sending my prayers and best wishes your way. Let me know if there is something else I can do to help you.
Bob

My response:

Hi Bob,
Thank you for your most kind note.
I am working a full schedule! I was out of the office and had to reschedule patients 2 or 3 days for testing, and am now being treated for a lymphoma. Although I may need to lighten my schedule on some days, by no means have I stopped working! I am undergoing treatment and expect a full recovery.
In the meantime, my fabulous associate, John Reuter is here and can see patients that don't work into my schedule.
Again, I appreciate your concern.
Joel

Everyone enjoys a story. When speaking of others, we

must always be careful with our words and report things accurately. While it doesn't seem necessary or even in good taste to send out a "Dear Colleague" letter to my referring doctors, Bob's misunderstanding is the result of my not doing so. I have continued to receive many requests for a consultation on patients, and have sent out numerous patient reports and letters to other doctors, so it should be obvious that I'm still working, but maybe Bob hasn't received such a letter lately. His intentions are certainly good, and I appreciate his concern. This is a good lesson in how rumors spread.

Given how I feel the week after my treatment, I can understand how others would expect that I would not be working during chemotherapy. But work is important to me. I love my job. Taking care of others gives me purpose in my life – a well-defined reason to get up and to get moving every day. Although it is difficult to be in the position of receiving care rather than being a caregiver, I don't feel the need to take a leave of absence from work. Still, I've decided to lighten my schedule during the week after chemotherapy. I will block out some time during the day so I can keep up with my dictation, assuring that I will be able to leave promptly when my appointments are finished. I also will block out a little more time over lunch, so if needed, I can take a short nap. If I'm going to feel subpar anyway, staying home would only make it worse. As long as my level of alertness is not compromised and I am able to continue to provide good care for my patients, I'm happy to be able to work.

This morning, a patient told me I looked good. I jokingly responded that she needed new glasses, but that I appreciated her words. Another, a bald man, told me I was catching up to him in the hair department. I told him we were engaged in a "race to the bottom" with respect to our hair. "I may only have around 300 hairs left," I told him, "but they are 300 of the toughest hairs you could possibly find!"

Monday, December 8
"He seems like himself."

My secretary Michelle told me that many patients expressed surprise when they checked out at her desk after their appointment. I suppose after reading my memo they anticipated that not only would I look different, but that I would not be acting in the way in which they were accustomed. My view is that if I'm not able to care for patients in a proper way, I shouldn't be at work at all. But it's more than that. I'm performing a bit of psychology on myself here.

In his book, *Strangers to Ourselves*, Timothy Wilson concludes that one of the most enduring lessons of social psychology is that behavioral change often *precedes* changes in attitudes and feelings. We become the way we act. In The King and I, recall the lyrics from the song, *Whistle a Happy tune:* "Whenever I feel afraid, I hold myself erect. For when I fool the people, I fool myself as well."

Additionally, in the Hebrew Bible, it is taught to "Receive everyone with a cheerful countenance." This teaching fits in nicely with the above premise. A pleasant demeanor starts every interaction on the right foot. This is especially important for me and for others who interact with sick people all day. Not only will the patient visit or any other interpersonal interaction tend to go more smoothly when it begins with a "cheerful countenance," but the very act of being pleasant, even if we don't feel good, tends to improve the way we feel. It may not make us feel normal, but it helps.

Over the years, I have often found that self-pity is

destructive, both physically and mentally. Patients who have been sick a long while and whose activity has been limited often descend into a vicious cycle. When they mope around the house, they become weaker, more withdrawn and even depressed. I often tell such patients that I want them to get dressed each day. I also tell many of them that I want them outdoors, even if for a short while, and even if they don't go anywhere. Just the act of seeming well can produce favorable psychological effects.

Circling back to me, it would be very easy some of these days to conclude that because I really don't feel good, I should stay home. Indeed, there may be a time in the future when I feel too sick to work. But if I'm well enough to go to work, I believe I actually feel better if I force myself to dress professionally, act cheerfully and "be myself."

As I think about these "rituals" of my routine daily life, I draw a correlation to Judaism as it relates to the importance of religious ritual. In a vacuum, the performance of religious rituals may appear to be empty and meaningless behavior. But instead, those who perform these rites and follow these customs have given themselves an opportunity for uniquely Jewish feelings to grow and develop. For example, as I mentioned in the earlier *D'var Torah*, many of us have distinct memories of our grandmother lighting the Shabbat candles on Friday evenings, and those who carry on this tradition find great meaning and comfort in carrying on this ritual.

I sometimes hear people say they are nonobservant because going to synagogue or performing traditional rituals has no meaning for them. But you won't win the lottery unless you buy a ticket! Doing comes before feeling. A person can read about how to ski, but they will not be able to engage in and enjoy the activity until they put on skis for themselves. No one will acquire even an ounce of spirituality or find an emotional tie to a faith by reading a textbook. Doing comes first. So rituals and behavior can create feelings. For me, the ritual of giving thanks when I awaken and get dressed to go to work actually helps me feel better than I would if I simply stayed in bed, thinking of all the things in my body that don't feel right.

Tuesday, December 9
The midpoint of the cycle.

I've lost several pounds over the past month or so. Looking at my small frame, we would all agree that this is not good. It seems obvious why people tend to lose weight during chemotherapy. The first 10 days of my treatment regimen begin with the infusion of the cancer-fighting drugs. After five days I then abruptly stop taking prednisone. Finally, I take two different antibiotics for another several days to combat any potential infections caused by the drop in my white blood cell count. The generalized weakness, loss of taste, nausea and loss of appetite in the days following my treatment conspire to cause a loss of weight, as happened after my first treatment. So the first one and a half weeks after chemotherapy are difficult.

Yesterday and today marked the mid-point of the cycle, and although I'm still required to wear a mask because of my low blood count, the symptoms have abated somewhat. I have a week and a half until my next treatment, and will try to regain my lost weight during this time. Already, my exercise tolerance during workouts has improved over the past couple of days.

Between now and next Friday, I must try to consume as many calories as I can (without antagonizing my gut – a tricky balance in those with Crohn's Disease) in order to put back the few pounds that I have lost.

I feel that if I can regain strength and weight, by my next and subsequent rounds of chemotherapy, I won't necessarily become progressively weaker with each treatment. I was told at the beginning of my treatment that the first two weeks after receiving chemotherapy would be very rough. So far, though, I seem to be feeling much better after 10 days, giving me another week and a half before the cycle starts again.

Wednesday, December 10
"I hope you're a good Christian."

A rather extraordinary spiritual event occurred in the office today. I'm sure Mrs. C. meant well in wishing me restored health. She expressed appreciation for the good care I have given her over many years and seemed genuinely sad when she read my patient letter and when she saw me. As I was about to leave the room at the conclusion of our visit, she looked at me, and in a clear voice, said, "Dr. Roffman, I'll be praying for you. I hope you're a good Christian . . . but even if you're not . . . (at this point she averted her eyes and looked off into the distance) . . . God . . . (at this point, she was clearly struggling with what to say, and concluded in a very soft, almost inaudible murmur) . . . will be with you."

Mrs. C. seemed to be having a theological crisis right in front of me! Would God indeed be with me, a good person in Mrs. C.'s view, even if I were not a "good Christian?" Her hesitation made me wonder if she ever had reason to question this before.

In Judaism, we don't have to worry about such distinctions. Our Talmud teaches that, "The righteous of all nations have a place in the world to come." Judaism accepts that there are many paths to God and righteousness.

Jewish scripture and literature refer to the soul inhabiting a "World to Come" after physical death. But whether or not one believes that there is a spiritual or even ultimately a physical existence following death, the point is that Judaism focuses on this world and on this life. Today's encounter with Mrs. C. crystallized the distinction between the mantra of Christianity, "Believe and you will be saved," and of Judaism. In Judaism, you are what you do.

Although there is an extensive body of teaching in traditional Judaism about a life beyond what we are conscious of, there is virtually no mention of it and certainly no emphasis of it during worship services in synagogues. Judaism's focus is on making this world better. On Yom Kippur, the holiest day of the Jewish year, it is traditional for able-bodied Jews to abstain from all food and drink for more than 24 hours. Instead of thinking about and engaging in worldly acts such as eating, bathing and working, we are to focus on repentance for our sins. We are to engage in *teshuvah*, literally "returning" to the ways of God, becoming better in body, spirit and deeds.

On that day, a portion of the Bible from the Book of Isaiah is chanted in synagogues. Of great significance is that in the reading, the prophet rebukes those who adhere to ritual purity only to sin against people. He admonishes them to ". . . unlock the fetters of wickedness . . . let the oppressed go free . . . share your bread with the hungry . . . clothe the naked."

Today, Mrs. C. seemed to struggle with the notion that only those who are "good Christians" will have God by their side. She ultimately concluded, though, that what we do as people counts as well.

Thursday, December 11
A letter from Mayo Clinic.

I received a letter this week from Dr. Ed Loftus of the Mayo Clinic. He has also been in touch with my gastroenterologist, Dr. Tom Rogoff. He expressed his sympathy for my plight and recommended a different medicine for my Crohn's Disease that might be tried after chemotherapy is concluded. The medication was tested at the Mayo Clinic, where Dr. Loftus was involved in its development. Because the effects of Remicade include the inhibition of the immune system, it may have been responsible for my lymphoma, and so I cannot be given it again. Like Remicade, the alternative is a biologic agent – a monoclonal antibody – but it is one that works locally in the intestines, and it has only recently been approved by the FDA. It works differently from prior drugs used in Crohn's Disease, and may not be associated with an increased risk of malignancy.

Because the new medication works only in the gastrointestinal track, it might not suppress the immune system, and I wonder if I will be able to take the shingles vaccine. I also wonder if it might be possible to take the yellow fever vaccine. (These are live vaccines, in which a weakened but living virus is injected into the patient. They should not be given to patients whose immune system is compromised.) The inability to take the yellow fever vaccine limits where Nancy and I can travel. It has never been a major source of concern to us – we've managed to travel to enjoyable and occasionally exotic locales, while excluding the Amazon River and other remote areas. Still, there may be a small silver lining to this entire illness if a window of opportunity opens some new travel sites. It was very thoughtful of Dr. Loftus to send the letter and communicate his recommendation for future treatment.

How fortuitous that this new medication for Crohn's Disease is available!

Last night, I noticed that my mouthwash had begun to regain its characteristic tingle. My taste buds are awakening after a lengthy slumber.

Friday, December 12
Something I have, not who I am.

I've had a good week physically. The protective surgical mask came off after Monday, and I feel normal both during the day and at night. Rather than the anticipated two weeks of feeling weak and nauseous, I had these symptoms for only 10-11 days this time, the same as I did after the first treatment. With my blood count up and because my strength is essentially normal, I've packed a lot of activities into the coming week – dental cleaning, breakfast with a friend on Saturday, two lunches and three dinners with other friends, an evening meeting for my shul, and an appointment with my gastroenterologist, Tom Rogoff.

By the end of today, I will have seen over 80 patients in the office this week. They all will have received the letter that explains my illness and appearance. Many do not raise the subject with me at all. Of the others, many tell me that I will be in their prayers. Many also tell me how good I look (to which I respond that they need their vision checked!). When I enter an exam room, my habit is to extend a warm greeting and get right to work. I let the patient bring up the subject of my illness, if they wish.

Lymphoma is something I have; it is not who I am. My family, work, religious affiliation, relationships and activities define my identity – not my being treated for a malignancy. This is just a passing distraction. I'm very happy not to be brought into a discussion of it with patients, though of course, I appreciate their interest and concern.

With respect to my treatments, I feel I'm in a good rhythm here at work and at home. The chemotherapy schedule and my response to it may prove to be rather predictable. I can handle this easily. The keys will be to avoid complications of the treatment and most of all, to have a good result. A week from today will be my follow-up PET scan. I'm already anticipating this test and hoping for a good result that reflects an effective response to treatment.

Saturday, December 13
"What if things don't go well?"

This morning, I had breakfast with a good friend, Craig Paul. I have known Craig since he first began his practice of Internal Medicine in 1983. In the course of our discussion about my lymphoma and Leah's wedding next fall, he asked me, "What if things don't go well with your treatment? What if you don't respond?" Only a good and forthright friend would ask this, and I appreciated the chance to put into words what I had thought about when I was first diagnosed. Although of course, I hope for a successful outcome, the possibility exists that my cancer will not respond and that my condition will deteriorate. Or perhaps a complicating and overwhelming infection will complicate my course, caused by the effect the treatment has on my ability to fight off nasty germs. Now I was being put to the test. Craig was the first to ask, "What if . . ."

"The wedding will go on, Craig. It would make no sense to change the date or the plans." I told Craig that if it was apparent that my life was in imminent jeopardy, I would prepare something in writing to be read at the wedding service, in which I would give some perspective on my life, the recognition that we all are here for a limited time, my admittedly poor sense of timing, my joy that Leah and Ross were being wed, and finally, my strong desire that the night should be festive. Leah and Ross will only do this once, and although the joy would be blunted to some degree because of my illness and absence, they should have a good time that night. I would encourage all the guests to do what they could to insure that the atmosphere was a happy and joyous one.

Craig told me, "It looks like you thought of all the things I would have thought about." I don't want to focus on the morbid aspects about my situation, but I would rather face the issue realistically and in a forthright manner, than pretend that it doesn't exist. It was good for me to talk with someone who wasn't afraid to bring up this tough topic.

Although I had thought about it already, discussing it with a friend is a good means of reality-testing. How do the ideas sound when spoken aloud? Is there another element that I'm not thinking about? Craig was pleased with my determination to face all the important issues with open eyes, and with my resolve to continue to do the things that are important to me. Craig is a straight shooter, and it was emotionally therapeutic to speak with him.

The conversation with Craig reminded me of key points made in the book, *Man's Search for Meaning*. In it, holocaust survivor and psychiatrist Victor Frankl discusses the triad of guilt, pain (emotional and physical) and illness, and the prospect of death. We face all of them in the course of our lives. Frankl teaches that we should transform the components of the triad into opportunities to maximize and optimize our human potential. So for instance during illness, we can resolve to create something positive as a result. Even if it is only to set an example of grace, courage and optimism, many will observe our reaction to illness. We have the opportunity to inspire people with our response.

In a similarly positive way, we can use guilt as an impetus

to change ourselves for the better. We cannot change the past, but we can change the future. And finally, because of the transient nature of life, we can and must seize the time we have to take action in helping family, friends, community, and the causes we believe in, helping to make the world a better place.

At services today, Rabbi Michele Sullum spoke about her family's trip to Israel and related it to the week's Torah reading. She spoke about how the wonderful memories from the trip will stay with her and her family as long as they live. She said something that I will personalize a bit and maybe say at Leah and Ross's wedding. Paraphrasing her, she said she used her memorable trip as a reminder that today's events will become tomorrow's memories. Some will be preserved into long-term memory.

So we should strive to have activities and to create stories that can be recounted and that become lasting, meaningful and pleasant memories in the future.

All in all, it was a very good morning.

Sunday, December 14
Willful ignorance.

I recently spoke with a childhood friend, Steve Sandberg. Naturally, he was surprised and saddened by the news of my lymphoma. As the conversation continued, though, I think I made him feel better by my optimistic attitude and my determination to continue exercising and working. When people ask what my medical outlook is, they are surprised when I tell them that I think it's relatively good, but I really don't know what the chances are for a complete remission. I have looked at some statistics in my medical textbook, but more in-depth research papers are available, and I have not read these. This is perhaps all the more surprising since as a physician, I have all sorts of resource material available to me. But even if I learned that the remission rate was high – for instance, 90% – I would relate it to my field of cardiology. If a patient is to undergo heart surgery, a 10% mortality rate for the procedure is considered very high.

My natural optimism would lead me to believe that I am going to be fine, no matter whether the quoted remission rate is high or a relatively low number. So there is no need for me to read further. I understand what can go wrong, and how I may be facing the prospect of a poor result. Nevertheless, I do not need to see the actual predicted numbers in black and white. I'm going to go through this course regardless, and learning what the statistics are will do me no good at all.

I received a note from a long-standing patient:

Dr. Roffman,
I admire the way you are handling your personal illness and, concurrently, still caring for your patients. I hope you can appreciate how much we respect you and the way that you honor your commitment to your profession.
You will remain in our prayers and we are praying for your return to good health and complete remission!! Be well, my friend....
Blessings,
C.N.

During patients' appointments, I don't bring up the subject of my illness, but if they wish to discuss it or ask questions, I am happy to respond. I recognize that there is a strong mind-body connection. I believe that patients with optimism and a sense of mission tend to have better outcomes than people who bemoan their fate and resent that they have a medical condition.

As I wrote earlier, a sense of optimism carries with it an improved medical prognosis. Similarly, there is a body of medical literature that shows that depressive symptoms are correlated with a less favorable outcome in disease. I intend to take full advantage of the benefits of optimism. My mission is to get better, so that I can take care of my family and my patients, and be able to serve my community.

My friend, Bassim Nathan, has called a couple of times in the past few weeks. Each time, he tells me that I sound strong, and that my attitude will help me heal. Bassim doesn't have a medical background, but he senses what the data tell us – attitude in and of itself may not heal, but it helps us heal. His calls have meant a lot to me.

Tuesday, December 16
Maybe the ultimate compliment from a patient.

Jim and I go back a long way. He is now over 90 years old. In the more than 30 years I have helped care for Jim, we've been through a lot together – Jim's coronary artery bypass surgery, his carotid artery surgery, and stories about his family. He served in World War II, and has periodically told me about his experiences. During this visit, he recounted how he was among the first soldiers to enter the Dachau concentration camp, and what he saw. Tears came to his eyes.

After I finished Jim's physical exam today, he said he had something to tell me. He is a very plainspoken man, and I braced for what he had to say. His wife began to cringe, because, to put in gently, Jim had lost some social inhibitions through the years, and she did not know what was about to come from Jim's mouth.

"I know you're Jewish," Jim began.

I became a bit nervous about what might come next. Jim

looked at me and finished his thought: ". . . But you'd have made a great Baptist!"

Wednesday, December 17
Important test coming up.

Although I try to put it out of my mind, I find myself repeatedly thinking about Friday's PET scan. I know how important the test is in determining my long-term prognosis. Although until this point I have resisted the temptation to read much about the statistics as they relate to lymphoma, I gave in to my curiosity and actually researched these results in the medical literature. The prognostic significance of the PET scan this week is quite strong.

If the PET scan shows lots of persistent tumor uptake, it does not bode well for me. The chances of a recurrence would be more than 50%. On the other hand, if there is very little or no residual disease, the long-term outlook is much better. I know that my heart will be racing as Dr. Naina pulls up the images on the computer screen. As much as I'll be looking at the images, I will be looking at the doctor's face for a hint as to whether he is pleased with the results. I hope that my lack of symptoms and normal energy level are indications that we're on the right track.

Thursday, December 18
Yosef Avraham ben Sippora and the Prayer Warriors.

It is a Jewish tradition that when someone is ill, his or her name is read in synagogue on Shabbat. At a specific point in the worship service, the prayer leader reads the names that have been provided to him by the shul. After the list is read, congregants have an opportunity to add names of their own. My friends attend Shabbat services at several different synagogues, and so my name is on these *"Mi'sheberah"* (One who blesses) lists around the city. In the prayer, the congregation asks the "One who blesses" – God – to bless the individual who is ill. Traditionally, the individual's Hebrew name is spoken, along with the Hebrew name of their mother. When the Hebrew name is not known, or if the person is not Jewish, the English name is read.

Dr. Hyman Tolmas came to the office with his daughter today. They brought individual holiday gifts for my office staff. What a thoughtful gesture! I came to the front desk to greet them and thank them for their kindness. Dr. Tolmas, who is a retired pediatrician in his 90s, looked at me and said, *"Yosef Avraham ben Sippora (Yosef Avraham* – my Hebrew name, *ben* – son of, *Sippora* – my mother's Hebrew name). I say a prayer for you every morning." It brought tears to my eyes.

For someone to express that much caring means so much to me. Cantor Zhrebker of our shul did the same thing when he saw Nancy a couple of weeks ago. He recited my Hebrew name to her and told her that he says a prayer for me every day. With so many patients telling me that I'm in their prayers, and with my name on the *Mi'sheberah* list of so many shuls, I only hope that God says, "Enough already – I'll heal him so you can all get off my back!!"

Soon after Dr. Tolmas's visit, I saw Cal, a long-standing patient. He told me he read the letter given to him by Michelle. "I wouldn't be here if it wasn't for you," he began. "I've already said a prayer for you." Then, in what I think was meant as a compliment, he continued, "I couldn't find a Jewish friend that I would love more."

Still another very touching message of caring came today. I received a note from a patient, telling me that in his church, the "Prayer Warriors" said a special prayer for me. Ten church members signed the note. I'm very grateful for all the notes and special wishes I've received.

Whether or not the prayers have an effect on God, they certainly have an effect on me. The best way for me to respond is to heal, and then to continue to do what I do – at work and outside of work.

Friday, December 19
Third treatment and the PET scan.

The wait for the PET scan seemed interminable. The wait for my lab work to come back so I could begin my treatment seemed interminable as well. Finally, the wait for Dr. Naina to come into the exam room dragged on and on. Each step of the process seemed to last for an eternity. As usual, I had brought a lot of reading material, but I had a difficult time concentrating on any of it.

Although I arrived for my PET scan at 7:30, it was close to 12:30 when Dr. Naina entered the exam room. It had been a long day already, and I had not even begun to receive my chemotherapy. I knew what was at stake and was anxious to learn the results. Even so, although I was impatient to learn of my results of today's important test, I was calmer than those late October days, with all their uncertainty. At least now, I was under treatment, and if it needed to be altered in some way, I was in the right place.

Finally, Dr. Naina came into the exam room, gave me a quick but friendly greeting, and before he sat down, said, "Your PET scan is clean. It's great." And just like that, the question was answered.

Dr. Naina then sat down and began to pull up the images on the computer screen.

"Clean? Normal?" I asked, a bit stunned at the sudden

turn of events. Maybe I just wasn't accustomed to receiving good health news. After all, the news I had received over the past few months was repeatedly bad.

As we looked at the scan, I probably asked him two or three more times . . .

"So you don't see any trace of the lymphoma?"

"So the pelvic bones and the leg bones look normal?"

"The scan is clean?"

Dr. Naina replied each time that there was no lymphoma to be found. "This is what we hoped to see and this is what we expected to see."

Dr. Naina was pleased. A simple fact that relates to every cancer patient: If the oncologist is happy, the patient is happy! Dr. Naina was happy with the results today, so I was very, very happy!

I told him that I had missed no work and that I continued to exercise, although at a somewhat lower level than before. "You are in great shape," he repeated a couple of times during the interview. He asked about the ringing in my ear, because I had sent a note asking if it would be okay to have the MRI scan that my ENT doctor requested. After a pause, and in his characteristically simple and direct way, Dr. Naina said, "We will look at your spinal fluid."

Uh-oh. It seems that there is a very small chance that the ringing (tinnitus) is caused by spread of the lymphoma to the brain. If that were the case, the current chemotherapy regimen wouldn't be effective, because the brain has a unique barrier to protect it against intrusion by medications. A different technique would be needed, in which the chemotherapy medications are injected directly into the fluid surrounding the brain. That would be an uncomfortable process, and the chances for remission would not be as good.

Dr. Naina assured me that the chances of lymphoma causing tinnitus were extremely small – only a couple of percent. He agreed with the assessment of the ENT doctor. The ringing in my ear was more likely just another manifestation of aging – as I tell patients, "gray hair" of the various organs in the body. Still, it is another procedure to go through, and an uncomfortable one at that.

The way to "look at the spinal fluid" is to do a spinal tap, in which a small needle is inserted into the lower back, and into the spinal canal. The area is first numbed by the use of a local anesthetic. This is not an enjoyable procedure, to be sure. The patient must lie flat for an hour after the procedure is completed, in order to minimize the risk of too much fluid leaking out, resulting in a severe headache.

We could, of course, just wait and do the MRI, with no other testing. But if we were wrong, and the tinnitus was caused by lymphoma, we would pay a steep price for the delay in diagnosis. It seems that an MRI is not as accurate at finding lymphomas as it is for discovering other, "solid" tumors. Looking at the actual fluid surrounding the brain was the best way to make this diagnosis. I told Dr. Naina that if he felt this was needed, then of course, I would be agreeable. He's the expert, after all. That's why I'm here.

Despite the prospect of another uncomfortable test, I left the exam room overjoyed. The long-term recurrence rate of my lymphoma is quite low, given its quick response to treatment. As if anticipating the next question, Dr. Naina told me that a full course of six treatments would still be administered, because with the lymphoma in the marrow when we started, I was in Stage 4 – the most advanced stage of cancer. That is fine with me – I'm not looking for short cuts and feel psychologically and physically prepared for a long haul. As I told him, I'm here to get the best possible results. Comfort comes second – a very distant second.

After I finished visiting with Dr. Naina, I was taken to a different room where I would have the infusion of cancer-fighting drugs. Because I had no unusual reactions to the first two rounds of treatment, the nurse increased the infusion rate this time. Still, I wasn't finished until late afternoon. It was a very long day at the hospital, but because of the good news, I left in a great frame of mind.

Saturday, December 20
Having a "why" to live.

Last evening provided another in a long list of reasons "why" I need to and want to live. Nancy and I are members of a group within our shul. The Hebrew word *havurah* is used for such an organized group that gets together for programs and events. Each year, our *havurah* celebrates the Jewish holiday of Chanukah by attending religious services on the Friday evening during the holiday, then having dinner at the home of a member of the *havurah*. After dinner, we have a "white elephant" gift exchange, where everyone brings an inexpensive wrapped gift, and all members get to choose one of the wrapped packages.

Unbeknownst to me, the group had secretly decided that this year, all the gifts would be for me. I was told to sit in a particular seat, and was handed one gift after the other. I didn't fully understand what was happening until after I had been told to open a couple of the gifts. It was absolutely overwhelming to me. The gifts ranged from Chanukah-themed socks to gift cards from ice cream shops and delicatessens.

As I opened each of the gifts, I tried to add a little mirth to the proceedings. Once I finished opening the last gift, I was able to gather my thoughts a bit and said a few words to the group. From the time I was diagnosed, many of these people called or emailed me to lend their support and to ask if they could be of help in any way. I told everyone that although there's no substitute for proper medicine (and some good fortune as well!), a strong support network, the right frame of mind, and strong motivation for healing have all been shown to improve the chances of a good outcome. Well, for sure, I have all of the above – now we just need to have a sprinkling of good fortune to seal the deal.

The German philosopher Frederic Nietzsche said, *"He who has a 'why' to live can tolerate almost any 'how.'"* I thanked them for being such a wonderful group of friends. Collectively and individually, they had given me yet another "why" to live. The moment was emotional for many of us, and several tissues were in use. During the time Nancy and I have been part of this group, we have frequently supported each other at the time of personal loss, such as the death of a parent. As I recall, though, we have not faced this particular situation before.

Sunday, December 21
A difficult Sunday.

As was the case after the first couple of cycles of chemotherapy, the hammer came down today. The nausea returned, accompanied by generalized weakness. Distraction is wonderful medicine, though. I felt a bit better after a small breakfast and after writing some notes, thanking my friends for the Friday night program. By late morning, I felt good enough to work out and decided to use my stationary bike. I was unable to exercise as long or as vigorously as I normally do, but even so, I felt somewhat rejuvenated when I was finished.

Later in the day, the nausea was still with me, though I got some relief with my anti-nausea medicine. Still, my appetite was poor, and eating dinner was more of an unwelcomed assignment than a pleasure. What little taste I still have is altered a bit, so things don't taste as they normally do. I anticipate 8-10 days of this, after which things will gradually improve. If the symptoms follow this pattern, as was the case with my first two cycles of treatment, I know that this will be the first of some rough days. I'm ready though, and at the end of this cycle I will be halfway done with my treatments.

As always, being with Nancy brightened my day. Calls from Mark always make me smile, and my cousin Sarene called to check in on me. I have many sources of strength that help the bad days become not as bad.

Monday, December 22
"It'll get worse."

Today was the third day after receiving my latest round of chemotherapy. As they say in cycling, today was a "tough day in the saddle." As I got ready to go to work, I had nausea, dry mouth with an altered and diminished flavor of food, weakness, indigestion, a flushed feeling, and loud ringing in my ears. I felt a bit better as the morning went along, but know that the next few days will bring more of the same. Of course, Nancy was quite concerned and supportive when I arrived home earlier than usual. I told her not to worry – I would feel better tomorrow. And if not tomorrow, then I would feel better the next day.

Last month, I discussed medical research in which the benefits of an optimistic attitude result in an improved medical prognosis. Today, my condition brought to mind a story in the Bible from the Book of Exodus.

After the Israelites escaped the Egyptians and crossed the Red Sea, we read that Miriam pulled out her tambourine and led the Israelite women in song and dance. Imagine Miriam in Egypt. Under duress to leave quickly, there wasn't even enough time to let the bread rise (And so Jews eat matzoh to celebrate their liberation – not exactly a culinary treat!). Still, Miriam packed her tambourine. It is as though she said, "Today is filled with tumult and uncertainty. But tomorrow, there will be occasion to celebrate, and I will be ready!"

So I told Nancy over a dinner that I had trouble eating. "Get the tambourine ready. We will have occasion to celebrate. Things will get better." She knew exactly what I was referring to, because I had brought up this story before, most often when I struggled with my Crohn's Disease.

Generally, my patients have been very supportive of my health situation. They seem glad that I'm still at work and leave me with good wishes. Many tell me that I will be on their prayer list. One patient this morning had a different reaction, though. When I told him that I had my third course of medications with three cycles still to go and that I was feeling the effects this morning, he nodded and said, "It'll get worse."

I could have probably predicted this response. Through the years, this particular patient has always seemed to look at the dark side of a situation. We all know these people. If the meteorologist announces that there is a 20% chance of rain on Sunday, people like this warn us that we had better change our outdoor plans because, "They're predicting rain." While some look for a silver lining, these people see only the dark cloud.

A few years ago, I gave a talk to a group of church volunteers. The topic was how we cope with adversity. These volunteers are among the finest people on earth. They belong to a group called the Stephen Ministers and help those in their church who are going through tough times in life, whether the cause is medical, personal, financial, or any of the typical hardships that we all face.

At the end of my talk, there was a question: "What do you do about people who are always negative? No matter what you try to tell them or how you try to help, they always see the down side of the situation. What do you do with people like that?" I thought for a while, leaned forward, and replied, "Avoid 'em!"

Wednesday, December 24
Rough start to the day.

I feel that the prednisone is having a big effect on my system. When I took prednisone in the past for Crohn's Disease I've had trouble sleeping, and taking it again brought back those unpleasant memories. When I got out of bed today, I felt fatigued, flushed, weak, and I had mild nausea.

Today our office would be closed for the Christmas holiday, so I spent time learning a new image-editing program for my photographs. I arranged meals to be brought to a congregant in my shul, and read articles from a couple of medical journals. I also arranged for Torah readers for this Shabbat, and reviewed the Shakharit portion of the Shabbat morning service that I would be leading. Then, I had a surprisingly good workout for 55 minutes on the elliptical machine, though at a lower resistance than usual.

After all that, I felt much better! I had a short nap after lunch, and then went to the bookstore with Nancy. It was not such a bad day after all.

The various mind-occupying and physical activities were distracting and invigorating. Tomorrow promises to be better still, as the chemotherapy drugs recede into the past. I have made a note to ask Dr. Naina about the necessity of taking prednisone for five days, and at such a high dose. Was the prednisone meant to blunt some of the side effects of the other drugs or does it have an independent effect on the cancer?

Nausea continues to be an issue. On a couple of occasions, I have awakened during the night sick to my stomach even if I took an antinausea pill at bedtime. After prior rounds of treatment, this has lasted 8-10 days, so I'll be glad when this period of time passes. My taste buds have also changed and things that normally taste good have an odd flavor, so it's difficult to find food that seem appealing.

I recall that during my first treatment, the infusion nurse suggested that I avoid all of my favorite foods for the entire duration of my treatment, because with the change in my taste buds, these items may suddenly not be appealing, and I might forever associate them with chemotherapy. They might then permanently lose their appeal. Still – all these months without ice cream? That's just not going to happen!

Friday, December 26
Signals vs. noises.

It's good to be back at work, even for one day before the weekend. The mask is back on as I am in my seven-day period of "semi-quarantine." The prednisone causes fluid retention, and I typically gain 4-5 pounds by the time I finish the course. As happened during my prior cycles, I lose that water over the course of a couple of nights after completing the five-day course of the prednisone. Last night began that process – I was awakened every hour or two to use the bathroom. The same pattern will likely occur tonight, and I will then be back to my "dry weight."

I've had so many new feelings in my body since my chemotherapy has begun, it's hard to sort out what is important and what is not. In the course of a typical day, people often experience all sorts of feelings – an ache here or a pain there. There may be a brief cramp in the abdomen or the leg, or a throbbing sensation in the head. The body is a dynamic organism, and no two measurements of any physiologic function are exactly the same. These reminders of our constantly changing inner and outer environment are simply "somatic noise." That is, they are sensations we all feel from time to time, are not important, and do not indicate that there is anything wrong.

Patients will frequently report numerous symptoms, and it is the job of the doctor to separate this "noise" from true "signals" that represent possible disease. Although it is sometimes hard for an anxious patient to discern the difference, I am guessing that virtually all that I'm experiencing is due to the medications and are the expected effects of the rapidly changing internal environment that the medications cause. I have created a mental catalog of these sensations, constructed a list of what I feel might be important signals and will discuss them with Dr. Naina during my next visit. The various chemotherapy concoctions have surely created lots of internal noise.

Sunday, December 28
The mouthwash tastes bad again!

A sure sign that my taste is returning occurred last night, when the mouthwash had its characteristic tingle and bad taste. This is very good news indeed! Today, I feel virtually normal – better than I have since just before my most recent treatment. As happened after the first two treatments, the generalized weakness, continual stomach distress and loss of taste lasted a little over a week. Today is day 9, and I would think that by tomorrow, I'll feel even closer to normal. I'll weigh myself in the morning and see if I'm a couple of pounds below my normal weight, as was the case before my first two rounds. If so, I hope I can regain the weight before I'm slammed again with the drugs.

Sundays are when I like to get outdoors on my bicycle. Although I felt strong enough to go on a ride, I am in the "semi-quarantine" period, and with a low white blood cell count, any cut or scrape could result in a severe infection. While I rarely have any incidents on the bike that would cause a break in my skin, why take the chance? So I will have to be content with an indoor workout.

Up until this point, my course has been uncomplicated. While difficult to endure, it has been simple. I have responded to treatment as well as I could possibly have hoped. Now, there are two additional tests coming up, and they are on my mind a lot. I certainly don't mind having an MRI and even a spinal tap, but the prospect that they might be abnormal is very worrisome.

Of course, I will do what I have to do to get better, but the finding of cancer cells in my spinal fluid would mandate a change in the treatment regimen, perhaps even requiring that the drugs be administered directly into my spinal canal. Surely the prognosis would be different, and the entire scenario is more than a little frightening. And although the MRI is not specifically looking for the lymphoma, other tumors can affect the nerve responsible for hearing, and the test might uncover such a tumor or an additional problem that is causing this awful ringing in my ears. If one of these is the cause of my tinnitus, a new set of issues and decisions will come into play.

As I wrote earlier, hardly anyone has a fully normal MRI. I'm certain to see findings that remind me that other processes are taking place in my brain that are abnormal and that remind me again of my aging and of the gradual physical deterioration that we all endure. The testing can't come soon enough – the wait seems to be the toughest part.

And speaking of that ringing in my ears, it is now in both

ears. I suppose that perhaps there is some good news mixed in with the bad. The bad, of course, is that the symptom continues to worsen, with no real prospect of a cure. What might be good news, though, is that it is very unlikely that lymphoma would cause isolated and symmetrical neurologic symptoms, with involvement of the nerves that go to both of my ears. Wishful thinking? Probably. I also hope that even though the chemotherapy didn't cause the ringing – after all, it started before I began treatment – it might just be that these strong medications are making the symptoms of the ringing worse, and so I hope the tinnitus will improve somewhat once I am finished with my course of treatment.

Tuesday, December 30
Numb fingertips.

During each visit, Dr. Naina inquires as to whether I am having any neurologic symptoms – pins and needles, dizziness, etc. I sent an email message to the oncology clinic today. The tips of my fingers have an altered sensation when I touch them and are just a bit numb. It seems that one of the medications in particular can cause this, and if necessary, the dose can be reduced. Oh well, just another cost of doing business. I hope the sensation is reversible. I will emphasize to the doctor at my next visit that my first priority, and far above all other priorities, is eliminating the cancer. I can live with some numbness in my fingertips. In fact, I can live with virtually any side effect that comes along with the treatment. My eye is squarely on the prize of recovery.

Wednesday, December 31
Thinking about repentance.

The mother of my secretary Michelle died two nights ago. I have had several conversations with Michelle, who is going through the intense grief that comes with the loss of a parent. Michelle had a difficult relationship with her mother, with unresolved issues and lingering resentment and irritation on both sides. From speaking with Michelle over the years, I know how hurt she has been because of this fractured relationship. There may have been no realistic chance that the issues causing the breach in the relationship could have been resolved, but she is now left with what will be life-long memories of a troubled relationship with her mother.

Even before facing this health challenge, I have often thought about my relationships. I do so a lot more now. Supposing the lymphoma has an intractable course and cannot be eradicated? Or what if I have a major complication, such as an overwhelming infection because of my low white blood cell count? Supposing I face the prospect of an early demise? Would I have similar feelings toward anyone as Michelle did toward her mother? Would I feel guilt and remorse that I hadn't tried harder to patch things up? Would I have regrets about how I treated someone and didn't apologize for those actions?

There is a story in the Talmud about a rabbi who tells his disciples to repent and reconcile with others on the day before they die. "But Rabbi, we can't possibly know the precise day on which we are going to die," the students respond. "Precisely," says the rabbi. I keep sifting through my "mental Rolodex," wondering what I should say to whom, in order to reconcile. At this point, I am very much at peace with my interpersonal relationships.

Some time back, a patient of mine took into her home and

cared for a long-estranged sister, who had terminal cancer. The sisters hadn't spoken much in many years, but now the sister, who had no other immediate family, needed Wanda's help. At her next office visit six months later, Wanda told me that her sister had died, but that she had remained in Wanda's home during the final months of her life. "After all those years with little communication," I began, "what did you talk about during the time she was with you?" Wanda replied in a very soft voice. "Missed opportunities."

As I search my mind for examples of those with whom I once had a close relationship but regret that I am no longer in touch or friendly, I am grateful that I am unable to find one. There is no one in my life with whom I have continual conflict, or whom I avoid because of past disagreements. Certainly, there are a few people with whom I am no longer friendly, but in none of those cases do I harbor regret. I have tried to cultivate friendships, to let bygones be bygones, and to appreciate the kindnesses shown me. This is comforting to me, because I would hate to know I need to reconcile with someone, and may not be able to.

The Jewish holiday of *Yom Kippur* is the most solemn day of the year. In the days leading up to this day, we Jews are commanded to repent for our sins, and apologize to anyone whom we have hurt during the preceding year. For those of us who take this seriously, the custom has a beneficial effect for the whole year.

The thought of repenting and of vocally and personally apologizing to someone before *Yom Kippur* conjures up an uncomfortable thought and action. So why let sinful, hurtful or insensitive behavior occur in the first place, and why let it linger once it has occurred? One can disagree without being disagreeable. So I try to be careful not to be personally insulting in the course of a disagreement. I try to separate the issue from the person. Maybe I'm not always successful, but as I think about the people who have been important in my life, I cannot think of anyone to whom I need to apologize, and for that, I am grateful.

Thursday, January 1
New Year's Day.

Because I must avoid crowds, celebrating New Year's eve was low key. Nancy and I usually go to the home of a friend where we usher in the holiday with lots of other people. This year, that was not the case. Instead, we had dinner with some friends, and then came back to our house where we all enjoyed each other's company.

Last week, a column in *The New York Times* by Arthur Brooks, the President of the American Enterprise Institute, wrote about how we should strive for "abundance without attachment," describing how our most cherished memories are not about things, but about experiences. There is certainly nothing wrong with material pleasures, he writes, but our ultimate happiness and satisfaction with our lives will be determined by things that cannot be quantified or counted.

During the holiday season, time and again I see patients who become emotional during their office visits. These people are typically distraught over broken relationships. As they express their sadness to me, their distress is never about the lack of wealth. Instead, they grieve the lack of closeness with those whom they crave to be near.

When Nancy and I get together with friends, I find it most enjoyable when we spend relatively little time talking about the "ornaments" in our lives, getting past the new camera or car very quickly. Instead, I like to focus on relationships and on our lives' experiences that have much more enduring value.

The way so many of my friends have reached out to me

fills me with gratitude that Nancy and I have cultivated these types of relationships.

In Abraham Joshua Heschel's book, *"God in Search of Man,"* he writes, "If the world is only power to us and we are all absorbed in a gold rush, then the only God we may come upon is the golden calf."

Friday, January 2
"You would never know ..."

We had a birthday party in the office for Vaishali this week. Amidst all the fun and laughter, I was asked how I was tolerating the chemotherapy. Overall, I reported, I have been doing fine. I then mentioned my tingling and somewhat numb fingertips, my occasional nausea and weakness, my fatigue in the week or so after the treatment, and my altered and diminished sense of taste.

Surprised that I had been dealing with so many symptoms, my office nurse Gayle said, "You would never know ..." I replied that if it was apparent to my office staff and patients that I needed to drag myself through the day, struggling to provide effective patient care and moping over my condition, I shouldn't be at work at all. If I am to accept the challenge and the responsibility of caring for patients, I need to be able to take care of those patients to the best of my ability.

I mentioned earlier that the Talmud teaches us to greet everyone with a cheerful countenance. There is much commentary about this. This teaching applies both to work and to one's personal life. Basically, there is a clear message that is transmitted when greeting someone with a cheerful smile. The person feels welcomed and cared for. Most people will respond in a similar way. A "ping-pong" effect is created. The entire interaction has thus gotten off on the right foot and has a greater chance of being pleasant and productive.

As this teaching applies to my job, the effectiveness of the doctor-patient relationship is at stake. A patient who feels listened to and cared for is more likely to be compliant with, for example, taking medications as prescribed. I am very aware that I am responsible for setting the mood of the office, and if I am not physically able to or am not in the proper frame of mind to set that tone, I simply should stay at home.

Sunday, January 4
Tough Cookie.

I've received numerous cards and emails from friends. I'm very appreciative of all the good wishes and prayers for my recovery. With each get-well wish I receive from a friend or colleague, the oppressive nature of my illness is mitigated a bit more. Each gesture of support provides a little more emotional buoyancy. I received a card from a family doctor, Katrina Bradford that brought a smile to my face and is my favorite. The front shows a chocolate chip cookie, and drawn on the cookie is a small smile and slanted eyebrows, giving the cookie a slightly menacing look. Under the drawing is written, "Tough Cookie." The inside is made to look like a dictionary, with "tough cookie" phonetically spelled out. Beneath it is the definition:

- *Someone with just the right mix of sweetness and strength.*
- *One who doesn't crumble under pressure.*
- *A fighter who's too busy kicking butt to sit down and cry, but knows it's okay to do both.*
- *A person who doesn't always ask for support, but has*

lots of friends who would do anything to help.

Inside, the card simply says, "Hang in there, tough cookie."

I sent a note to Katrina, thanking her for the card and telling her how much it meant to have her take the time to think of me.

Many people are uneasy about calling someone who is ill or who is grieving. Maybe they're not sure what to say and they feel uncomfortable. From my experience as a physician, a parent who has suffered the loss of a child, and a patient who is coping with cancer, I understand the importance and the impact of simply reaching out. The conversation can be very brief – perhaps simply an expression of sympathy, empathy or just concern. But that gesture of care is important – an expression of caring that touches someone when they need it most. The call doesn't need to be long or intrusive. Just a simple expression of concern is adequate, and will almost always be appreciated.

This week, I've had additional calls from friends who conveyed their concern and good wishes.

Tuesday, January 6
"I'll pray for you."

I have had any number of patients tell me that I'm in their prayers. I always express appreciation for this sincere expression of caring. But one type of response always puzzles me a bit. When some learn that I am scheduled to have a particular procedure, they respond that they will pray that the test results are favorable. Tomorrow I will have an MRI of my brain, and this will be followed with a spinal tap on Friday. Does it make sense to pray about the results? Whatever is causing the ringing in my ears is already there. Praying that it is a benign process doesn't make much sense to me. What's done is done.

So for what, then, should we pray? As I have sat in my shul many hours since being diagnosed with lymphoma, I have thought much about this question. In truth, it's a subject of much discourse in Judaism. I have written a *D'var Torah* on this subject, and here are some excerpts from the teaching I presented to the congregants in my shul.

. . . Well, I know what type of prayer DOESN'T work – the type where, while awaiting the results of a biopsy from the doctor, you pray that it will be just a benign growth. Or, seeing smoke from your neighborhood as you drive closer, you pray that if there is a fire, it will not be YOUR house. This type of prayer is a combination of health or property insurance and magic. There would be no order in the world if things could be randomly changed after the fact. This is fantasy. It's not how God or our universe works. We know that our universe is reliable. Rules of nature can't be broken willy-nilly . . .

. . . And praying to a benevolent personal God, who is omnipotent, a force for goodness and all-knowing? One that will cure and eliminate evil? All we have to do is read the newspaper each day, and we know that God doesn't work in this way, either. There's simply too much misery in the world.

*God works within the rules of nature to give us an intuitive sense of the optimal choices we must make in our lives, based on justice, love, connectedness and our own experiences. Rabbi Brad Artson of the Ziegler School calls his philosophy "Process Theology," and teaches that our prayer is not to coerce God or to petition God with prayer; not to deputize God to do the things that we should be doing ourselves, but rather to give us the strength and the insight and the courage to do the things **we** should be doing.*

Rather than use prayer as an introspective seeking, an opportunity to explore within what is most important, an expression of gratitude and an opportunity to feel a connection with our tradition and our people, the meaning, purpose and relevance of prayer has become concealed and confused. In many instances, our prayer book fosters this notion.

So why bother with all of this – the room, the trappings, the rituals, the customs, the surroundings, the Hebrew, the fixed liturgy? It is because they all serve to bind us together, reinforcing community and generation-to-generation emotions and linkage . . .

We all understand that as we read some of our prayers, we must simply let our intellect recede a bit. Reading many of the prayers in our prayer book, we may find it obvious that we cannot take some of these prayers literally. Maybe they serve best to "get us in the mood." Much as athletes "warm up" before the actual competition or a violinist practices with scales before her actual performance . . .

Like so many other experiences, we can read about prayer, think about it and make judgments about it, but we can't fully assess its relevance and effectiveness until we give it a chance, and do it. Although, as with any endeavor, we would like to resolve our philosophical issues before committing to action (or prayer!), the empirical order is just the opposite. Belief and feeling won't emerge out of an intellectual discussion alone. Coming together to pray, celebrate, even to grieve, gives us an emotional underpinning that ties us together as a community and as a people.

*Rabbi Elliott Dorff writes that through petitional prayer, we give expression to our desires, and also learn in the process to recognize what we **should** want and what we can do to achieve it. We are forced to acknowledge what others need, and how we can help. Those who aren't open to the idea of a future filled with choices and changes are stuck* *with predetermined endpoints – in fact, they create their **own** limits.*

Prayer may be a difficult practice to acquire, but it has great potential for teaching us about Judaism, about ourselves, and maybe even about God. Abraham Joshua Heschel wrote, "It is in moments of prayer that my image is forged, that my striving is fashioned."

The Jewish tradition teaches that the future is not predetermined. We have a role in creating a future that is worthy of us and of our heritage. God wants us to be a partner in creating a better future, but it depends on us. The choices we make change the future. God works through us, and allows us – mandates us, really – to make the right choices. God is waiting for us and depending on us . . .

So my prayer will not be that the findings of the tests are benign. That has already been determined. Rather, it will be for me to have the strength to cope with whatever might be found. It will be that I have the sensitivity and insight I need in order to help my family through whatever tough times await us. That's one type of prayer that God can definitely help me out with.

Wednesday, January 7
MRI of my brain today.

I jokingly have told my friends that I hope there is enough brain matter for analysis. I don't anticipate that a malignancy will be found and don't even expect that a benign tumor affecting the nerve responsible for hearing is lurking. But I dread the commonly reported "age-related atrophy (or some such phraseology)" that the test may uncover. While this would not be life threatening, it would be a psychological blow to realize that my brain was showing signs of age.

The test itself was quicker than the last MRI I had, because that one covered more ground – my leg and pelvic bones. Today's test was so noisy, though, that if I didn't have ringing in my ears before, I would surely have it now.

Sometimes, it is several days before a radiologist interprets the study, reports the result to the referring doctor, and the call is made to the patient with the results. Since I asked Dr. Tang to order the study, and knowing how quickly the results of my prior MRI were reported, I hope that I receive a call within the next day or so.

Thursday, January 8
"No abnormalities found."

The call from Dr. Tang came last evening – the MRI is normal! No tumor, either benign or malignant, was found in the brain. Even more good news: there was no mention of age-related atrophy (shrinkage). Whew! The last step in making sure the ringing is not due to my lymphoma is the spinal tap tomorrow. This will hopefully reassure us that lymphoma cells have not entered the spinal fluid and attached to the lining around the brain. Although Dr. Naina feels this is unlikely, he wants to be sure, and of course that's fine with me. With no tumor in the brain, it seems that the ringing in my ears is most likely due to simple age-related changes. My hope is that the chemotherapy is compounding the problem. Of course, it may be months before I know for sure.

On a lighter note, Nancy wants a second opinion about the MRI. She told me that the radiologist doesn't know my brain like she knows it, and it's anything but normal!

In the office today, a patient told me how he uses my example in his Sunday school class. I had mentioned to him during his last office visit what I've already written about: how a simple phone call or note from a friend brightens my day. I often try to let people who are sick or who are going through tough times know that I'm thinking of them. A little time expended results in a large dividend.

Most people appreciate the gesture of caring. It takes but a minute to send off an email or to make a call, but people remember those small gestures. In philanthropy work, this is called stewardship – an organization simply can't say thank you often enough to its donors. And when donors are thanked and feel appreciated, they tend to respond with a stronger allegiance to the organization. Similarly, friendships also need stewardship. Letting someone know they are being thought about means the world.

I have received so many calls, texts and emails in the past few days – from a hospital chaplain, from friends with whom I haven't chatted for a long time, from people offering to bring dinner, and from my office staff. Some even remember my treatment schedule.

Nancy and I have had offers for Shabbat dinner as well. The response has been overwhelming but unobtrusive at the same time. And with each one, I feel a sense of support that gives me yet more strength. Electronic communication has made it very easy to let someone know you care. And this simple act reaps enormous returns.

Friday, January 9
"Hit me with your best shot. Treatment number 4."

I anticipated (and had) a long day. My spinal tap was in the Zale Lipshy Hospital, so it was in a different building from where my chemotherapy is infused. The radiologist explained the procedure (including the dreaded, "You'll feel a little burning.") and began to numb the area of

132

my lower back by injecting local anesthetic into the area through a tiny needle. Another small needle would then be inserted to drain off spinal fluid. The fluid would be analyzed for cancer cells. There was no general anesthesia used, so I was fully awake. I was positioned on my side, which was a little awkward, but not very uncomfortable. Memories of when I performed spinal taps while a house officer in Hartford Hospital flashed through my mind.

The procedure was not painful. The "burning" of the numbing medicine was only a pinch in my skin. The doctor then numbed an area much deeper – closer to the spinal canal. The discomfort from that injection was not burning in nature, but was more a visceral, deep pain. It was quite uncomfortable, but brief.

The procedure went very smoothly. After the spinal tap was completed, I was to lie flat for an hour. There is no way to close the small hole in the tissue that had been punctured, and the most common complication of the spinal tap occurs when fluid sometimes continues to leak out of the spinal canal after the needle is removed, resulting in an awful headache. To minimize the chances of this complication, the patient lies flat for a period of time, and activity must be restricted for a couple of days.

After the hour was up, I made my way over to the cancer treatment center for my chemotherapy. A couple of short hours later, the infusion nurse handed me the initial report of the spinal fluid. No cancer cells were detected! Although some additional testing would be done on the fluid, it was now extremely unlikely that there was lymphoma lurking in my brain or in the spinal canal. Another hurdle has been cleared. Dr. Naina spoke with me soon after I received the written report from the nurse. Though not surprised, he was of course pleased that we now had a clear path to the finish line.

I discussed with Dr. Naina the tingling and numbness

in my fingers. These symptoms had become quite uncomfortable and are classical for what is called a "neuropathy" (a disorder of the nerves that are responsible for sensation in the fingers). They are known side effects of the cancer drugs. Though not severe or disabling, they were definitely new. Dr. Naina nodded knowingly and said that he would adjust the dosage of one of the medications.

He also told me that this neuropathy may or may not get better. I fully understand this, and also told him that I can live with most any side effects from the treatment. My first and most important priority was getting rid of the cancerous cells, and that if he felt that continuing the culprit medicine at its full dose gave me a better chance of achieving that goal, then "Hit me with your best shot!"

Living itself is a higher priority than having perfect feeling in my fingers. But Dr. Naina was not concerned with the dosage adjustment and reassured me that it would not adversely impact my treatment. He also told me that it was possible that this medication was making the ringing in my ears worse. I hope that is exactly what is happening, and that indeed, it is reversible.

We also talked about the prednisone, which causes restlessness at night and fluid retention. Dr. Naina told me the high dose for five days is needed. At this dosage, the medicine has an independent and beneficial effect in eradicating tumor cells. No problem, then. High dose prednisone it is.

This was a very long day, and I'm glad Nancy and I turned down some dinner invitations from friends. When I finally returned home, I was tired and cold, and I had abdominal discomfort, slight nausea and weak legs. It was a good night to stay at home.

Sunday, January 11
The response to misfortune or illness.

Yesterday, I led our synagogue in Shakharit – a portion of the Shabbat service just before the taking out of the Torah, in which we express gratitude for living and affirm our faith. It was the first time I led this portion of the prayer service, and I planned on leading this set of prayers on this particular day because it was the day following my treatment. The task required much preparation over the past couple of months.

I realize that the day I chose for this inaugural event may have been a bit masochistic, but by focusing my energy on something constructive, my attention was diverted somewhat from my illness and the difficult treatment it entails. In a similar way, on several occasions I have volunteered to present the weekly teaching, or *D'var Torah*, on the day or week following my round of treatment. Again, this requires much preparation and involves a 6-10 minute presentation.

In Judaism, the response to death is life. We are taught to commit ourselves to life-affirming acts often as a way to honor the deceased and as a way to respond to misfortune. By acting in this way, death and misery do not have the final word.

In a similar way, the response to illness can be a renewed commitment towards something positive. What a distinctive and wonderful way of approaching adversity – finding some way to channel energy, renew spirit and honor the afflicted by engaging in acts that help others, by learning and by keeping a hopeful attitude.

A direct act that will benefit others, such as a donation to a charitable organization, is a common such response to honor the deceased or to respond to a friend's illness. For me, this means continued work helping to care for those who are ill in my medical practice. It also means continued involvement in my religious community in positive ways, such as helping to coordinate our shul's Mitzvah Meal program, which I spoke of earlier, or teaching the lessons of our tradition in a way that will be uplifting to others.

So my choice to lead *Shakharit* was to demonstrate that the response to adversity is to perform a life-affirming act – to mitigate the bad with something very good. When possible, adversity should not have the only word, the last word, or even the predominant word.

Monday, January 12
"Do something good for someone else . . ."

Today was very difficult. As I have come to expect, I feel progressively worse during the first few days after chemotherapy, then very gradually feel better after a week and a half. The nausea, ringing in the ears, weakness and fatigue are tough to handle. One of my patients this afternoon was a 79-year-old woman who still works as a realtor. She has been battling a significant heart problem and I have seen her frequently over the past couple of months. Today, she felt much better than when I last saw her, and so I think we finally turned the corner.

She asked how I felt and how I was able to continue with a full work schedule. I replied that I do try to lighten my schedule a bit during the first week after chemotherapy, and that although I realize I am going to feel bad, being home wouldn't help. As long as I'm mentally clear and can help others, working is what I should be doing. She had a wonderful response: "Do something good for someone else and you help yourself." This is not only true in a medical sense, but is especially accurate in a psychological sense as well.

Wednesday, January 14
"No one has a monopoly . . ."

Many patients express surprise that I've gotten sick. They note my physical conditioning habits and my slim physique. Of course, they may not know about my Crohn's Disease and subsequent Remicade treatment, with its attendant risks for infection and malignancy. Certainly, it would be a bit inappropriate to go into all this with patients. Instead, I simply respond, "No one has a monopoly on good health." There are no guarantees. These things happen when they are least expected. One day, I felt fine. The next day, my legs hurt. Who knew? Who could have foreseen this?

In the blink of an eye, our lives can change. The unexpected and unwanted telephone call. The other car that seemed to materialize out of thin air. The invested money that vanishes with a bankruptcy filing. The pain in the legs that seemed to have no discernible cause. These are great examples of why we should learn to appreciate the blessings in our lives while we are able.

The week has been very tough. While I don't feel that I've gotten progressively weaker with each treatment, some of the side effects are cumulative. For instance, my sense of taste has never really returned to normal, so that the most recent round of drugs further compromised my taste.

Combined with the low-grade nausea that comes along with the chemotherapy, I need to remind myself that food is medicine. Hunger is a luxury. "Just eat," I tell myself. Mealtime might take longer than usual, but I try to follow these orders. Similarly, the neuropathy has not resolved, so that the effects of each subsequent round of medications adds to the existing numbness and soreness in my fingertips.

Yesterday was the last day of the five-day course of

prednisone. I seem to hold on to around five pounds of water with each treatment. It all seems to come out at night, beginning the night after my final dose. So I expect that tonight and tomorrow night I will beat a steady and repeated path to the bathroom. If previous patterns hold true, I will be up hourly to rid myself of some additional water.

I'm into my fourth cycle of treatment now, and officially "over the hump." The halfway point has been crossed. Once I'm able to navigate the effects of last week's treatment, I will have only two to go. The end isn't quite in front of me yet, but I've turned the far corner.

Friday, January 16
Home care? I don't think so.

The medical case manager from my health insurance company called today to see how I was feeling and how my course of treatment was unfolding. My medications and testing will be very expensive, and my healthcare providers will present my insurer with a large bill. The case manager seemed genuinely interested in how I have been doing, but the cynic in me makes me feel that she called to be sure I was compliant with the regimen and am not doing anything to lengthen the course. I mentioned how I have been trying to keep up my nutrition and workout routine so that I don't "spiral downwards" with each subsequent round of medicine.

She made me aware that if I can't go to work because of nausea, I have benefits that will cover home care and intravenous fluids. Good heavens! I reported to her that I am working a full schedule. Unless I was essentially bedridden, staying home was not for me. I would just feel sorry for myself. No, I need to be productive as long as I am able. I'm not trying to be a hero and I certainly don't feel that my choices in this regard would work for everyone, but I feel that the best way for me to get through this course of treatment is to keep to as normal a schedule as possible, with concessions made as necessary.

Last night was very difficult. As was the case with prior rounds of treatment, I was awakened every hour or so as my retained fluid worked its way out of my body. Falling asleep after this brief excursion took a bit longer each time, and I didn't feel rested when morning arrived. After prior rounds of treatment, it took a couple of nights to achieve my "dry weight," so tonight promises to be a repeat of last night.

Sunday, January 18
Home stretch . . . not!

I got a nice note from a patient, telling me that I was now in the home stretch of my treatment. I suppose this is a way of dealing with adversity – telling oneself that it's "almost over." Going through my fourth round of chemotherapy with two left, I know this is not the home stretch. For me, that will arrive after I receive my sixth and final treatment, though even then, I will still face a couple of weeks of its effects. For now, I'm just starting to feel a little better after my most recent infusion. After another week or two, I will be slammed again for round five. Late next week, I will be 2/3 done with my chemotherapy, so I certainly don't feel as though I'm near the finish line at this point.

But then again, I often play mind games myself when I am on a long bike ride. The distance between completing 1/2 of my planned route and 2/3 of the route is longer than between 2/3 and 3/4, and so on. Mathematically, I try to figure out how many miles it will be until the next fraction in the sequence, with each succeeding fraction coming sooner than the one before. In a way, this treatment is a bit like that. Whatever gets me through is fine, I guess. I may be turning the far corner, but I'm not yet in the home stretch. There are still too many bad days ahead, too many chances for infection, too many days of fatigue and nausea, too many days of wearing a mask and not being able to even go out to dinner with Nancy. But every day brings me a bit closer to the completion of the treatment course.

Tuesday, January 20
The ambivalence of anticipation.

A patient today told me that before I know it, the treatments will be over, and I will be feeling much better. While that may be true, I don't know whether to be happy or sad about what I hope will be a seemingly quick passage of time. While I certainly look forward to the day when my lymphoma and its treatment will be in the rear view mirror, I hate to look past weeks and months, and point to some future event as being what I wish for. The implication is that I simply have to "get through" the intervening time, and soon enough, the endpoint will be reached. My problem with that outlook is that I hate to look past any day at all.

It's both a strength and a weakness of mine that I hate to waste even a minute. So to look ahead in anticipation of some event or marker of time might imply that I am simply biding my time until my treatments are finished. I don't want to miss, for example, Monday, February 2. That would be the third day after my next treatment. I know I won't feel good at all on that particular day, yet the idea of just getting through that and other days is abhorrent to me. Who knows what else might happen on that day? What sorts of experiences, interactions with patients and friends might I miss if I just bypass that day?

Abraham Joshua Heschel teaches that every moment presents a unique opportunity in life that will never again occur. Each moment is precious. I don't want to wish away any day – even days that I know will have unpleasantness.

An especially inspiring portion of the Torah for me is when God tells Abraham, "*Lech lecha*," – Go to a place. Abraham doesn't know where he will be going. He is told to leave all he knows – his family, his home – and go. A great unknown awaits. A great adventure is about to begin. Yet Abraham was completely unaware of what was in store for him at the time. That passage continues to motivate me. We are all Abraham. We don't know what the future will bring. We don't even know what will happen in an hour. Yet, this passage inspires me to go into unchartered waters, to challenge myself and leap into the unknown.

In that way, I will continue to be driven to grow and to affect people and the world in a positive way. I reject the notion that the coming weeks and months will have more negative moments than positive. Why is that so obvious? Who knows what good will happen during that time? Or even in the next week? Why would I want to take a chance on missing it?

So although when the time comes I will fully appreciate the conclusion of my chemotherapy and the reversal of all the ways it makes me feel unwell, I don't want to miss any potential adventures and experiences between now and then. This is what I will call experiential ambivalence. I want to continue to have many experiences over the next couple of months (but admittedly, I would just as soon miss some of the ones I know are in store for me). So if the question becomes, "Would you like to just close your eyes and magically skip ahead to March 1 (when my treatment will be over)?" My answer would be no.

Friday, January 23
Food is medicine. The battle with my home scale.

As I proceed through chemotherapy, I remain acutely aware of what can go wrong. While I remain confident that we will have a successful outcome, the possible complications are never far from my mind. I'm thankful for every day, and am appreciative of those around me who are supportive and kind. Practically every day, I receive a reminder of how friends and family care for me. Just yesterday, I received a note that Shelley and Simma Weiss donated a leaf on our shul's "Tree of Life" plaque, in the "Fervent wish for a full recovery and a long, healthy life ahead." It's such a blessing to know that people care, and encourages me to remain steadfast, spiritually and emotionally strong, and to regain my physical strength as quickly as possible.

My fifth treatment is coming up this week. For the past several days, my appetite has been closer to normal, so I'm trying to put back the couple of pounds that I regularly lose after chemotherapy. It's a continual battle, but I don't want the three-week intervals between treatments to result in cumulative weight loss.

I find myself trying to follow the advice I've given so many patients in similar circumstances, when they simply don't get hungry in a normal fashion. One of the telltale signs of a patient's deteriorating condition, and a marker of a poor prognosis is weight loss. "Food is medicine," I tell these patients. "Hunger is a luxury. You don't have to be hungry to eat. As long as it doesn't make you sick, just take a bite at a time, and take in those good calories."

This is wise advice that I find myself following for more

than a week after my treatments. Meals are a chore. The combination of altered taste and a very poor appetite make it very easy simply to not eat. But I'm very aware of the downward spiral that can result: loss of weight from poor nutrition results in more weakness, which results in yet more inactivity, debility and additional weight loss. It's critical to intercept that spiral and change the trajectory. Maintaining weight and activity, and keeping those parameters as close to normal as possible, is vital in the course of an extended illness.

Sunday, January 25
A tough but appreciated bike ride.

Today's bike riding conditions were not optimal. The weather was cold (44 degrees at sunrise) and windy (10-15 mph, from the north), and the ride was tiring (44 miles, after not riding outdoors for 6 weeks). But in the end, it was exhilarating and psychologically healing. I had a great time with my friend Ron Steiner.

Since the time of my diagnosis, I have tried my best to stay in good physical condition, with workouts at home. I normally follow the same basic workout schedule each week, with a combination of various exercises. After each round of chemotherapy, my routines are shorter and less vigorous. As time passes and I feel less of the weakness from the chemotherapy, the routines become a bit more vigorous and closer to what I have been accustomed to, though I have not been able to get back to what I consider my "baseline." Still, I have been able to do some workouts almost as strenuously as before the treatments started. Then, the cycle starts again.

It was great today to be able to go on a long ride. Normally, my bike rides are longer, but given the weather conditions and my lymphoma, I'm very pleased.

Tuesday, January 27
"They get worn down . . ."

Each year, I participate in a benefit bike ride for the Multiple Sclerosis Society. The ride takes place over two days and covers 150 miles. This year's route is actually 160 miles and will take place, as always, during the first weekend in May. At the starting line, I tell the other riders, *"This is as good as we're going to feel for days!"* At this point in my treatment routine, the psychological battle is in full swing. Although I no longer have nausea, I continue to have a number of issues related to the chemotherapy – changes in appetite and taste, neuropathy and fatigue – not to mention the symptoms from my Crohn's Disease and the unresolved, bothersome ringing in my ears. As I look ahead to the next treatment in a few days, I realize that *this is as good as I'm going to feel* for the next couple of weeks. And if this is as good as it's going to get, the bad is going to be plenty bad. That's why it's so important to keep up with other interests and activities.

I can understand how people become "battle-fatigued" in their fight with cancer. There are more side effects from the medications than there are actual medications. A radiologist who treats cancer patients described to me how patients typically get worn down both physically and psychologically as the treatment schedule progresses. It's very important to not let this happen. We patients need to keep our eye firmly on the prize: hopefully the gift of additional time to spend with our family and loved ones. I feel that I'm generally handling my course of treatment well. But wow – quite an ongoing challenge.

When I began receiving treatment, some who haven't

been through chemotherapy would tell me, "It will be over before you know it." Well, it has already been a long few months. It will be early March before I finally start to feel better. This hardly would qualify as a "before you know it" length of time, considering that I started in early November. I still have a couple more periods of wearing a facemask and an increased risk of infection. There are still more periods of nausea that I will need to endure. But this is simply what I have to go through to get better, and I remain grateful that we have the medications that will give me a good chance of having a remission.

Thursday, January 29
"I'll leave Jesus out of it."

The Talmud teaches that the righteous of all nations shall have a place in the "World to Come." (The "World to Come" is Judaism's euphemism for what will become of us after we die. It is thus named, but not described, and certainly not emphasized in Jewish religious prayer services and teachings.) I don't feel that only Jews have the correct and sole "pathway" to holiness. In the eyes of Jews, non-Jews are only obligated to obey the seven commandments given to Noah (Among others, these include injunctions against theft, murder and animal cruelty, and the pursuit of justice) in order to be considered holy.

I would certainly never feel that a Christian's prayer was less meaningful than that of a Jew. I don't view prayer as a call to God with a specific request that will either be answered in the affirmative or in the negative by a great supernatural power, and I am very happy to have people of all religions pray for me. I take the prayers of others as an expression of their sincere wish for the restoration of my health.

Today, I was moved when a Muslim woman told me that I would be in her prayers. She said, "You took such wonderful care of my husband for many years (he has since died)." Earlier in the week, a Christian man asked me if I would allow him to pray for me, adding that he "would leave Jesus out of it." Although I was a bit amused by this, I still told him that I would be honored and humbled to have him pray for me, using whatever wording he thought was appropriate. As we consider our relationships with people of other faiths, it seems that there is much more that unites us than divides us.

Friday, January 30
Treatment number 5. "You are a superstar!"

Thankfully, I have only one more round of chemotherapy to go, and that's a very good thing, because the infusions themselves are becoming more difficult. I was nauseous while receiving the medications today, and that had not happened before. I was also extremely tired for several hours afterwards, but a walk around our neighborhood with Nancy and a dinner with friends perked me up.

My appointment with Dr. Naina was informative. He told me that my chances of staying in remission for at least several years are greater than 90%. He also said that, although we will do periodic blood tests, there would be little in the way of testing that would help us know if I had a recurrent lymphoma.

The plan is for me to have a PET scan one month after treatment concludes. This will serve as a baseline study, and we can then compare it to a later study if symptoms recur. PET scans, though, are so sensitive that any minor tissue injury or inflammation could be misconstrued on the scan as a possible tumor, and would prompt hand-wringing and perhaps unnecessary testing, biopsies, etc. So routine PET scans will not be done beyond the baseline study.

So how will we know if the lymphoma recurs? It is very unsettling to think there is no test that is both sensitive (able to identify recurrent tumors without missing any) and specific (meaning that what looks like a tumor is indeed a tumor, rather than something else – an injury an infection, etc.). In my case, my lab values were normal even while the tumor worked its way through my bone marrow, so routine bloodwork would be of questionable value. If I have a recurrent tumor, though, it may behave differently, and my lab studies may be abnormal. Routine and periodic blood work, then, is probably the best screening measure we have.

In medical journals and discussions, screening tests in general have come under some question. Tests as wide-ranging as mammograms in relatively young women, PSA testing in older men, and even the once routine chest X-ray have had their utility called into question. In my case, a routine PET scan or MRI may well result in more questions than answers.

I clearly have what Dr. Naina calls a problem with my immunoregulatory system, putting me at increased risk for a malignancy. Lymphocytes are part of the immune system, and in my case, a particular cell line within this system began to reproduce uncontrollably. In essence, that is what cancer is – uncontrolled reproduction of a particular type of cell. Now that I will no longer take Remicade, that problem may be mitigated a bit.

Meanwhile, we are resetting the "cancer clock" back to zero. The malignant cell line has been eradicated. It would be very unlikely that any lymphoma cell could survive what has been a chemotherapeutic onslaught. Dr. Naina is confident that we have completely eliminated all of the cells associated with this cancer, and so another cancer would mean the proliferation of another cell line.

I feel very good about how the treatment has gone so far. I simply need to avoid infections and take the same approach of maintaining weight and strength. When I told Dr. Naina that my weight is close to baseline and that I biked 44 miles last weekend, he said, "You're a superstar!" Coming from a cancer specialist, that's music to the ears of any patient.

Sunday, February 1
One more month.

It was approximately three months ago that I began chemotherapy. In a few weeks, I will have my final treatment, and so a month from now, I should be starting to feel better after that infusion. A month can be a long time, but with Leah's birthday during February, and a nice celebration in our shul in a couple of weeks to celebrate Nancy's birthday, there is also much to look forward to, and that will be my focus.

The MS150 bicycle ride is a two-day event that supports the Multiple Sclerosis Society. I have participated in the ride 17 times and have raised tens of thousands of dollars for the MS Society in the process. Last year alone, I raised over $11,000. And how symbolic: The Hebrew word for life is *chai*. In the Hebrew language, numbers are represented by letters, with each letter assigned a numerical value. When it is spelled out in Hebrew, the letters that represent the number 18 spell the word *chai*. So *chai* is thus a Hebrew word of great significance and one that is prominent in modern Judaism. In fact, the Hebrew letters of the word are often used as a visual symbol representing hope, faith and life itself. If I can do it, this would be my 18th MS150.

What a great surprise I had yesterday at Shabbat services – Ron Steiner and Eli Baron told me they wanted to participate in this year's MS150. Ron told me he knew how much the event meant to me over the years. Given my illness, he assumed I would likely miss it this year. He therefore wanted to ride in the event in case I could not, to "carry the flag."

I replied that I had every intention of riding in the MS150 this year, and would be delighted to have him and Eli JOIN me – not SUBSTITUTE for me. As though I needed more motivation to do the ride this year! It will be great fun having a couple of partners to ride with, although my course may be a bit shorter than it has in the past. I will reach out to some of the others in the *kehillah* to see if there is anyone else who might be interested in riding.

The three of us had a conference call last night and worked out some of the logistical details. Soon, I will need to formulate a plan for the ride. The average rider is much younger than me, and out of the approximately 2,000 riders, there are usually only a couple of dozen my age or older. Under the best of circumstances, this is a difficult physical and mental challenge, with many hours spent in the saddle. I may need a somewhat revised plan of attack this year. Normally, I train quite vigorously all year-round and am ready for the challenge the bike ride presents. This year, though, is unlike other years.

Monday, February 2
A litany of complaints.

Today was difficult. I had all the usual and by now expected side effects from the chemotherapy, making it difficult to get through the day. Sleep is difficult on such a high dose of prednisone. I have generalized fatigue and malaise, probably as a result of the lack of rest and the medications. My fingers are tingling, and at times, the ringing in my ears sounds almost like screeching freight trains. My tongue is a bit numb, and what taste I'm left with is altered, so that nothing tastes quite right. I have low-grade nausea that is mostly controlled with medication.

There. I got all that off my chest. Tomorrow will be better. I keep reminding myself that this is just what I have to go through to get better, and get better I must. So I have no complaints, and just made this list for the record. I remain grateful that we have medicines that can take care of this problem. I have changed my office schedule this week, allowing for some short blocks of time through the day to enable me to work at a somewhat slower pace, and to ensure that I will be able to complete all my dictation before leaving the office, so I don't have to rush to the office the following morning to complete my work.

Wednesday, February 4
Why so many rounds of treatment?

If the PET scan after the second treatment showed no trace of cancer, why are four additional rounds of chemotherapy needed? There are a couple of reasons.

First, a few cancer cells may have remained after the second infusion and may have been beyond the ability of the PET scan to detect them. If the treatment was then stopped, the remaining cells could multiply, and the process would begin all over again. This would have completely negated the progress made by the treatment that had already been given.

Additionally, we must understand that although medicine has made breathtaking progress in treating so many diseases, that progress usually was made incrementally, typically in small steps. The combination of drugs that constitute my chemotherapy regimen was brought together because of the individual and collective properties of those chemicals in fighting and killing cancerous cells. The specific dosages, timing of the treatments and the number of treatments was tested using a very specific protocol. A standard was thus established and a response rate was measured. If that protocol is breached, there is no assurance that the same results will ensue.

As time goes on, changes in the specific protocol I am receiving will likely be made and then tested against the protocol now in use. Some of these changes will probably be borne of necessity, such as in debilitated or elderly patients who cannot tolerate the rigors of six rounds of very strong medicine. Others will come about as the result of new drug development and experimentation. It may well be that at some point, fewer treatments will be given or that fewer drugs will be used.

The protocol that I received has a track record that is very good. As long as I am able to withstand the effects of the treatment, we dare not take the chance of altering what has been an effective plan of attack on the cancer.

Friday, February 6
A difficult week.

This has been a very difficult week. I'm not sure whether the effects of the chemotherapy are cumulative or whether I'm battling a psychological battle, but I haven't rallied as in the past. Maybe the fact that I've been battling allergies with respiratory congestion has added to it. Normally, by a week after treatment I begin to feel better, but not this time.

I noticed that my blood count has been slowly but

steadily falling with each treatment, so that may well be an indication that the medications are building up in my system. The anemia may well explain my reduced capacity to exercise this week. Today is day 7, and with the weekend coming up, I hope that a couple of days off work will help. Combine that time off with a couple of good workouts, and maybe by the beginning of the week, I'll begin to feel back to my old self. This will have been a very long four months, but the final treatment is in view, and it can't come any too soon!

Monday, February 9
Response to patients.

I'm beginning to feel better. I have more energy and I am a little stronger overall. Actually, this is right on schedule, as it is day 10 after my latest round of medications. The valleys seem to be a bit deeper as treatments continue, but I begin to climb out around the same time each cycle.

I have had a lot of practice responding to patients' reactions when they see me in the office. Here are a few of their reactions, and my responses:

Men with little remaining hair sometimes comment that I now look more like them. I respond that, "We're having a race to the bottom." Or maybe, "As you have found out already, hair is overrated."

Many patients express sadness at my plight. I tell them that I'm thankful that we have medicines that can effectively treat this condition and very often restore good health. Medicine and the physicians who are knowledgeable in their use are sources of strength.

Patients often tell me that, because of my bike riding and healthy appearance, they are surprised by my illness. I respond that sooner or later, health challenges come to all of us. Just as I expect of my patients, I'm battling this with all the tools at my disposal.

Others express surprise that someone who takes care of others and does such good things can be stricken with misfortune. I respond that no one has the promise of indefinite good health, and no one has an assurance of good fortune.

Occasionally, patients will tell me that they are surprised that I don't look sick. My response is that I'm not sick – I just have some bad cells in my bone marrow that require strong medicine in order to eradicate them. But sick? No, I'm not sick.

As I wrote earlier, the Talmud teaches that it is beyond our power to explain the good fortune of the wicked or the misfortune of the righteous. I don't consider myself righteous, nor do I consider that I am a sufferer, but the point is as I already expressed – one cannot predict what the future will hold.

Thursday, February 12
A (tentative) plan.

The MS150 bike ride is now less than three months away. It seems that a lot of patients have asked me this week whether I'm still biking. As I wrote in an earlier post, Eli and Ron will join me for this two-day event. In my exam rooms, where photos of recent MS150 bike rides hang over the counter, I have been asked several times this week about the ride. It's time to formulate a plan for this year, though of course, it might change.

Here's my plan, tentative though it might be: The first day's course is 86 miles. The rest stop for lunch is at the 50-mile mark. In past rides, that first day has been difficult, and although I'm ready to ride the next day, I'm very tired when I cross the day 1 finish line, and it takes all the energy I have to complete the 86 miles. So I think I'll call it a day at the lunch stop and take advantage of the "half-day option," hopping on a shuttle bus the MS Society provides, and ride the bus to the finish line. (The MS Society mainly wants to raise money for MS, so they try to make the ride as easy as they can for everyone. By providing rides for those who wish to stop, they prevent the event from being a mandatory ultra-endurance test. Buses and vans are provided for those who cannot or choose not to bike the entire course.)

The second day's ride has been lengthened this year, enabling the finish line's location to be in Sundance Square in Ft. Worth. This is a course that was used several years ago, and is longer than the course that has been used the past several years – 75 miles rather than 66. Again, I've been able to finish this course in the past, but the last time was seven years ago – long before my battle with lymphoma.

The shorter first day should enable me to complete the second day, and finish to a grand celebration in Sundance Square. Riding a total of 125 miles over the two days seems like an ambitious plan, and I realize there will be no shame if I am not able to ride that distance. The event is, after all, a fundraiser, and I can certainly do that.

After completing my treatment and depending on the weather, I will have five or six Sundays to train. And of course, I will be able to exercise more vigorously during the week at home.

The gauntlet has been thrown – both the mental and the physical one. Now let's get that last treatment done, so the recovery clock can start to tick!

Sunday, February 15
A slower than usual bike ride.

G reg and I met to do some bike riding today. Normally, I ride around 15 miles before we meet at Arbor Hills. We then ride for 15 miles together, and then I ride home. The length of the ride home depends on how I feel, the weather, the time of day, etc. While today's ride was a very respectable 49 miles, it was decidedly slower than usual. Why was I having a tough time keeping up with Greg?

I kept looking down at my tires. Were they low on air? No – the only thing that was a bit low was my power and stamina. My riding speed was slower than usual, the result of less riding and exercise than usual over the past several months. Maybe some anemia is responsible as well. Still, this was a respectable distance today – it just took longer to do it. I'm very confident that things will improve a lot over the next few months, as soon as my final treatment is completed.

Tuesday, February 17
Nancy's birthday.

T he absolute toughest part of the whole course of my illness has been knowing how much Nancy has suffered. How I hate to be sick, knowing how much she cares and hurts for me.

In my cardiology practice, patients sometimes become despondent and tell me that they have nothing more to live for. Typically, these patients have been sick for a lengthy time, and they don't see any more good that can come from their lives. Very simply, they don't enjoy living. I point out a loving relative who either has accompanied them to their appointment or who they have told me about during one of their prior visits. "That's why you need to live," I tell them. Their life and their comfort still mean much to that particular loved one. "If nothing else," I say, "You must do what you can to make them happy."

The very best way I can help Nancy and lift her spirits is to get better as quickly as possible. She has tried with all her might to make me as comfortable as possible. She has filled my life with her love and, importantly, with fun. Even on the bad days, we still typically try to share a laugh. I feel that remaining optimistic, and maintaining my normal activities as much as possible are all key factors in reassuring Nancy that I will recover, and in making each day as pleasant as possible. The medications will do their job. Nancy has been supportive in all these aspects of my course, and I am beyond fortunate to have such a loving and committed partner.

Wednesday, February 18
Theater of the absurd.

In the last two weeks, three different elderly women have gotten a little too close for comfort. It's one thing to be told how sexy it is to be bald, and how this "Yul Brenner Look" of mine is very attractive because, well, he was quite the sex symbol. But today took a bit of an uncomfortable turn. While I was examining an 81-year-old woman (granted, she was more vigorous and youthful than the normal 81-year-old, but still . . .), she told me that, "Bald men really turn me on!" Taken aback – no – dumbfounded, I paused in the exam, returned to my stool at the computer and replied, "Yes, well, let's go over your medications." Good grief!

Part Three

Final Treatment And Its Aftermath

Friday, February 20
The sixth and final treatment.

Normally when I'm in my car, I listen to the radio: news, sports, jazz – whatever fills the need at the time. On my way to UT Southwestern today, the radio was turned off. The traffic was heavy and the ride took longer than usual, but it didn't matter. I had many, many thoughts racing through my mind, competing for attention. For a few minutes, one train of thought would wander through, only to be supplanted by another.

First and foremost: this is the anniversary of my son's death. How would George have reacted to my illness? What would his response have been? What would he have told me? Actually, I feel that I know the answer. He would have reacted just as he did with his own illness: it's no one's fault, it's just nature. Let's get on with treatment. Let's continue to live as normal a life as possible. The illness is what I have, it's not who I am. And he would have found humor in as many places as possible, such as with the elderly women "hitting" on me. What a loss his death was, and is. It leaves a gulf that can never be filled. My enduring task is to honor him and his memory the best way I can.

In Judaism, the answer to illness and to death itself is life. In the prayer we repeat on the anniversary of a loved one's death, the Mourner's *Kaddish*, nowhere is death actually mentioned. We accept death as part of life; it is a natural extension of the glory and magnitude of life and nature. The *kaddish* is a life-affirming prayer.

In his short life, George impacted many people and involved himself in many worthwhile activities. I am compelled to do whatever I can to continue his ways. I constantly strive to do things that would make him smile, and, in the best teachings of our Jewish faith, engage in *tikkun olam*, the healing of the world, trying my best to make the world better.

I also thought of all that I have done during these four months of chemotherapy. I have been a supportive husband, father, brother and friend. I have cared for hundreds of patients to the best of my ability. I have learned two parts of our Shabbat worship service, and led my community in prayer. Through Congregation Shearith Israel, I have coordinated meals to be brought to several families. I have exercised and have planned to continue to raise charitable funds for the Multiple Sclerosis Society in the upcoming MS150 bike ride.

Life is so precious, that even though the chemotherapy has compromised me, I haven't wanted to miss anything! Four months – even four days – is too long to withdraw. Life doesn't wait. There is too much to be done, too many new challenges, too many people and things upon which I can have a positive impact.

I thought of how fortunate I am to have such a loving

wife, of the repeated calls and expressions of love from Mark and Leah, of the repeated texts expressing support from my nephews Jeremy and Gary, the dinners shared with friends, the many calls, texts and emails from relatives and friends, the way people have reached out to me during my entire illness. All passed through my mind in a big jumble.

I thought of all the things coming up after my treatment. Tonight: an evening with a group of friends. Dinner is shared on Friday nights with these eight friends every month or two. Tomorrow, Nancy and I will attend the birthday party for our dear friend, Ruth Schor. Nancy and I have known the Schors for over 30 years. They are not only fun to be with, but they care about others, and it's a privilege to share in their event. I will take photographs during the party, and hope to be able to make a book for them.

On Sunday I will participate in a charity indoor bike ride to support ovarian cancer research. Normally, I bike through the entire event – six hours. This year, I'm going to try to make it through one solid hour. Still, to be involved at all is a challenge and an honor. Through all these activities, I will be battling the side effects of the cancer medications – weakness, fatigue and low-grade nausea. But I have learned to compartmentalize all of that, just go on with what needs to be done, and to derive as much enjoyment from all of them as I possibly can.

All of these thoughts continued to compete for my attention even as my appointment began. First came the drawing of my blood. While I waited for the results, Dr. Naina came into the exam room and we discussed again the plan from this point. There is a small chance the cancer could return – small enough that screening tests involving imaging scans would likely cause as much harm as good. We also chatted about the various side effects I was experiencing from the chemotherapy medications. While they cannot be ignored, they are simply not going to get the best of me. Our plans will continue with no changes in store: I will have a PET scan in four weeks and my Mediport will be removed following the end of the course of treatment. Periodically, I will have blood drawn and will return for appointments as the doctor sees necessary. Whatever I need to do, I will do.

I have a vivid memory from sometime in the 1960s of the TV sports announcer Curt Gowdy describing San Francisco Giants pitcher Juan Marichal's seemingly increased strength as he pitched in the ninth inning with a lead in the game. He seemed to actually increase his pace, despite what must have been near-exhaustion. Gowdy said that Marichal was "smelling the roses." I believe the analogy is from horse racing, where the winning horse is covered in bouquets of flowers. I'm not quite smelling the roses yet, but check back in a week or so.

Sunday, February 22
A letter.

Doing good things for others even when feeling bad can be inspiring to others. This note came from my friend Gail Greenberg, after I had just visited her father, who is recovering from surgery:

Joel, it was a delight to see you today, and I was honored that you shared what you have been going through with us. We are praying for you and rooting for you and are relieved and encouraged by your good test results. I'm sorry that you and your family are having to go through this ordeal. I can't imagine how difficult it is, but you are getting better and healing yourself with courage that inspires us.

Thank you for taking the time to visit Dad. We all enjoyed being with you so much. Meanwhile, be well, and keep up the good work that you do to help others in your medical practice and in the bikkur cholim/meals program. Every day you make the world a better place.

Monday, February 23
Leah's birthday.

Is it possible that it has been 30 years since Leah was born? So quickly! I've read that the single biggest surprise of everyone's life is how quickly time seems to pass. With any milestone birthday, there is some ambivalence. We see our lives moving along more and more quickly and are unable to slow the sands of time as they drop through the hourglass. Today, though, there is only joy. A few months ago, Leah became engaged to be married to a wonderful man. What we all want for our children is for them to be settled and secure. We want them to be healthy and educated, morally upright and honest, and of course, compassionate and loving. Leah is all of the above.

This fall, Leah will marry Ross in a traditional Jewish ceremony. There is no ambivalence today, only happy thoughts of Leah dancing through my mind. Speaking with her today filled my heart with pride at her sensitivity, intelligence and maturity. And while nobody knows what tomorrow will bring, Leah and Ross can realistically face the future with optimism and anticipation. Of course, we don't know what the future will bring any of us, but the teachings of our tradition help us face this uncertainty with strength and determination.

Thursday, February 26
A great victory?

Since my final chemotherapy treatment last Friday, several friends and relatives have commented to me that I have now "won" my battle against cancer. I understand that this is their way of coping with my illness. They desperately want a sense of finality to my treatment, and to be able to label me as "cured." I truly appreciate their affection for me and their support through the course of my illness.

I'm afraid I don't share the sunny outlook, though. First, my weakness, loss of taste and appetite, and nausea this week feels nothing like a victory. Next week and in subsequent weeks, I will feel better. Even considering that, though, there is no final victory against illness. Only in fairy tales is there a "happily ever after." Not to cast a dark shadow on the results of my treatment, but I am now entering an interlude until the next battle. No one gains a final victory against illness.

Hopefully, this interlude will last a long time and will enable me to enjoy my family and be available to love and support them for many years to come. It will also enable me to pursue my other interests: taking care of patients, and serving my shul, the Jewish people and my community. Still, the number of my remaining days of life will be fewer tomorrow than today. I have but one life, and the Jewish tradition teaches me to make the most out of it.

Although there is a large body of Jewish teaching about the *olam habah*, the "World to Come," the subject is not generally discussed in synagogue. We Jews simply don't focus on it. Nowhere in the Torah is it discussed in any detail. In Judaism, we are focused on how we act in this world, and we should not anticipate any specific rewards for acting in accord with God's teachings. The Torah commands us, "You shall be holy because I am holy." In Judaism, goodness is defined by how we act.

Sunday, March 1
Involuntary Inspirational.

A friend of mine in shul, Mike Raboy, told me what an inspiration I was. He was aware that during my months of treatment, I set out to learn to lead the congregation in the preliminary portions of the Shabbat service. I assured him that setting an example was purely involuntary, and in no way was I looking for accolades. Still, it was a very nice compliment. My nearly normal work schedule, engagement in volunteer activities, and challenges I took on in my shul belied the existence of a serious medical problem. Far from draining me of strength, though, I believe maintaining the various elements of my life helped me immeasurably.

In his book, *To Heal a Fractured World*, Rabbi Jonathan Sacks, former Chief Rabbi of Great Britain, writes, "When we suffer, there are two questions we can ask. The first is, 'Why did this happen to me?' The second is, 'What then shall I do?' So different are these questions that they generate two distinct types of culture. The first focuses on the past, the second on the future. When I ask, 'Why did this happen?' I see myself as an object. When I ask, 'What then shall I do?' I see myself as a subject. The first is passive, the second active. In the first I search for someone or something to blame. In the second, I accept responsibility. When I do that, a profound human dignity is born."

"How can I make the best of this day?" rather than, "How am I feeling?" is the question that becomes paramount. Certainly, there are days in which illness prevents us from achieving anything beyond attempting to heal and seek comfort. The patient should not be made to feel guilty for illness, and in many circumstances is unable to fully engage in other activities. But to the extent possible, the healing process can be aided by having a mission, even if the mission is to be a model of courage and grace in adverse circumstances.

Tuesday, March 3
No sense of finality.

Reactions from friends and family to my completing my course of chemotherapy have been understandably celebratory. Of course, there is reason for relief as I begin to feel better while knowing that I'm not going to be hit with another round of medicines that will weaken me yet again.

I view my life through a different prism, though, from the way a healthy, younger person might. This illness is not the same as a broken arm suffered by a teenager, where the removal of the cast signifies the end of a health setback that now allows the patient the prospect of many years of uncompromised health. Instead, I am left with the realization that the medication that allowed me relief from the worst symptoms I had from Crohn's Disease, Remicade, can no longer be used. While there may be an effective alternative treatment, I nevertheless approach the coming weeks and months wary of the possible setbacks that might occur.

A person in his 60s must view good health with gratitude, but with the awareness that the biologic clock continues to tick, and that the next health setback looms not far in the future. I don't mean in any way to be pessimistic, but I have been chastened by this experience with cancer and by my observations of thousands of patients through

164

the years. The reality is that, alas, no health victory lasts forever. The conclusion of my treatment does not bring a sense of finality. Although I have an optimistic nature, I understand that we are all here but for a limited time and must view each day as an opportunity that will never again be repeated.

Sunday, March 8
No more chemotherapy on the horizon!

I am now into the third week following my last round of chemotherapy. In the past, every time I reached this point, another treatment was looming in the upcoming week. This time, though, there is no such weapon aimed at me. The nausea is gone, though my taste is still altered. The numbness in my fingertips is better, though not completely. The ringing in my ears remains a constant and unwanted companion. I am definitely hoping for gradual and ultimately complete resolution of these symptoms. My weight is still a few pounds below what is normal for me, but after what I've been through, that's not unexpected.

This week, I will have an appointment with my Dallas gastroenterologist, Dr. Rogoff. We will discuss the advisability of beginning the new medication for my Crohn's Disease. As I wrote earlier, I would like to be able to delay beginning this treatment until my normal immunity returns and I can have the Shingles vaccine. Dr. Naina told me that it would be at least six months before my immune system returns to normal, though. I have been having some abdominal pain, and am uncertain if it will be possible to wait that long.

Friday, March 20
PET Scan and doctor's visit.

Today's routine felt almost as though it was a victory lap. I was fully confident that the scan would be fine, since I already had a normal one before my third treatment. Following my now-familiar routine, after completing the PET scan, I walked over to the infusion center for my appointment with Dr. Naina. I donned the mask, assured the receptionist that I had not been to Africa in the past 21 days, and waited in the large waiting room for my name to be called. Scanning the mask-covered faces in the room, I was struck by how cancer is a disease that shows no preference to age, gender or ethnic origin.

Dr. Naina bounded in to the exam room, and in his usual manner, blurted out the results even as he was logging on to his computer. "Your scan is very good. No tumor." There. Done! We looked at each frame together, side-by-side with the first scan. All of the abnormal areas of the original study were now gone. It was as though the ornamental lights on a tree had been turned off. His recommendation was that I have a periodic check on my blood and visit with him in the clinic every few months, but he knew that I would be seeing my gastroenterologist and internist periodically and would certainly be attuned to any unusual symptoms that might come up, and said, "You're a busy man. There is really no need to come here to see me after this summer."

He again explained that no imaging studies were needed, because these studies are sensitive to any type of inflammation, and that any change in my system, no matter how small or minor would result in an abnormality. If I had no symptoms, "What would we do then?" he asked rhetorically. I was to report any unusual pain that lasted longer than it should. In other words, I was to ignore what I felt was the ever-present "somatic noise," but if I had a notion that the discomfort was not noise, but rather a "signal," I should call and make an appointment.

With that, we parted ways. I expressed my sincere appreciation for his care. The calls and text messages then began. The three immediate calls were to Nancy, Leah and Mark. Once in the car to drive home, the texts to friends would of course have to wait. My mind was racing, though, with an ever-expanding list of those with whom I wanted to communicate. So many people had gone out of their way to show concern and to be supportive, and I wanted to be sure to reciprocate with a message of good news, just as I had shared bad news months ago.

Happily, the remainder of the day was quite routine. After the warm embrace from Nancy and hugs from all the office staff, the day was filled with patient care. The box of unused facemasks could now be returned to the supply closet. My name could now be removed from the "*Mi'sheberah*" lists of the various shuls in which my Hebrew name was read for the past several months. That is one list on which no one wishes to be included.

Sunday, March 22
Feeling normal.

It has been a long time since I felt normal over the course of a weekend. I have no leg discomfort and face no diagnostic tests. There will be no chemotherapy causing significant side effects, and it is wonderful that I can now focus on health maintenance rather than recovery from cancer.

Yesterday, I read the *Gomel* blessing in shul – an expression of thanks that is said when one has survived a potentially threatening situation such as a long trip or a significant illness. In many ways, my fellow congregants shared in my illness and now they happily shared in my joy. As I sat in shul and mentally scanned all that I had been through, I at first envisioned a boxing match in which chemotherapy drugs were in one corner, making me feel sick, and all of my emotional support "teammates" – family, friends, Judaic teachings, my own determination – were in the other corner, making me feel good. I quickly realized, though, that rather than opposing one another, they were working in concert to enable me to heal.

Today was my first bike ride since last summer when I actually felt good. This week, I will schedule a time when my Mediport can be removed.

Monday, March 30
Four Questions.

Later this week, we will celebrate Passover, and Nancy and I will have 19 people for our ceremonial meal – our *seder*. Although it pales in comparison to the time it will take Nancy to set the table and prepare the meal, I have had lots to do as well, in trying to make the *seder* enjoyable, informative and inspiring. A traditional part of the *seder* is the chanting of the "Four Questions," in which it is customary for the youngest person in attendance to ask what makes this particular night different from all other nights. During a teaching session on leading a Passover *seder* taught several years ago by Rabbis Gershon and David Glickman (a good friend who has since moved to the Kansas City area to lead a congregation), the rabbis suggested that the *seder* should be interactive and proposed that the *seder* leader send some additional questions ahead of time to those attending the *seder*.

Although I changed the questions somewhat over the years, I have been following their suggestion since that session. Last week, I sent out my own "Four Questions" to our guests, asking them to be prepared to discuss their answers during the course of the *seder*. A couple of the questions will have a special meaning for me this year. Here are the questions for which I will ask each of our guests to prepare answers:

1. In what way are you grateful for freedom this season, where in the past you were "enslaved?" What "shackles" have been removed from you in the recent past?
2. In what way are you still a slave, "yearning to be free?" To what are you still "shackled?"
3. For what do you say *dayeinu* (it would have been enough)? What are you most grateful for?
4. What will you do in the coming year to be a redemptive force in the world? How will you "repair the world" so as to bring about the messianic age that we pray for?

Sunday, April 5
Survivorship, yet sadness.

A couple of weeks ago, Suleika Joauod wrote a piece in the New York Times in which she describes her feelings of loneliness, sadness and depression following the completion of her treatment for cancer. It might seem surprising that these emotions are very common in such patients. One would ordinarily expect that such a patient would feel exhilarated after being pronounced cancer-free. What gets in the way of joy? There are several possible factors:

- A new and intense feeling of bodily vulnerability. The

body has betrayed her in the most impactful way. Unlike other illnesses she may have had, this one was accompanied by a "mortality rate." Far different from high blood pressure, arthritis or even pneumonia, this one placed her squarely facing possible death. Could the body ever be fully trusted again?

- Withdrawal of a once-attentive support network. During the initial diagnosis and throughout treatment, friends and acquaintances embraced the patient with an outpouring of concern and help. This "secondary gain" is often such a strong elixir that many patients find it difficult or impossible to cope with its withdrawal.

- Lingering after-effects of the cancer-fighting medications. Hair growth, strength, taste, normal sensation in the fingers are just a few of the many possible bodily functions that may take a long time to fully recover. They are constant reminders that, although treatment is finished, the body has gone through enormous stress and trauma.

- Maintenance medications are sometimes associated with unwanted side effects. Just when patients think they are finished with the awful effects of chemotherapeutic agents, they are subjected to additional substances that are constant reminders that there is a lethal enemy lurking around the corner.

Dr. Kevin C. Oeffinger, the director of Memorial Sloan Kettering Cancer Center's adult long-term follow-up program is quoted in the article, "We like to think of the end of cancer treatment as the closing of a chapter, but what most people don't realize is that the emotional struggle continues long after. Feelings of post-treatment depression and anxiety are amazingly normal."

How can these post-treatment feelings of sadness, anxiety and depression be avoided, or at least coped with? Here are some characteristics and habits of people who seem to have avoided the "post-cancer blues," gleaned from my years in medical practice and from my own personal experience.

- They understand that a true support network should consist of those closest to them. Those in this "real" network didn't disappear after treatment was finished. Many people may have sent notes or made a phone call or two, but although their show of concern was certainly appreciated, they understand that acquaintances, even friendly acquaintances, are not the same as close friends and close family. They constantly cultivate family ties and friendships that are deep and lasting, transcending the vicissitudes of life. People who are truly close don't "disappear" once treatment is completed.
- They ask tough questions of their doctors so that they understand the rationale for post-treatment testing and medications. They understand the benefit and possible side effects of drugs that are taken after chemotherapy is completed.
- They frequently reached out to those who reached out to them. Many took advantage of this opportunity to establish and grow new and deeper relationships with people.
- Some found the need to seek help for lingering sadness or feelings of depression or hopelessness. Counseling and/or medications can be a big help, both in the short term and in the long term.
- They accept the limitations of the body. Alas, we are not immortal. Sooner or later, illnesses befall everyone. They have learned, as we all must, to cope.

- Maybe most importantly, they had a mission, or purpose in their life. They were able to manage their illness and were eager to be done, so they could carry on with the most important elements of their lives.

Monday, May 4
The MS150 Bicycle Ride.

The benefit bicycle ride for the Multiple Sclerosis Society is now complete! I had been thinking about it for months. As planned, I completed a somewhat shorter course the first day than in prior years – a concession to the longer route this year and to the aging process. The two-day route covered 160 miles this year, 10 miles longer than in the recent past. I last rode this particular route in 2008 and even then, it took all the strength I had to complete it.

Although it was very difficult for me to get off the bike while I still felt strong, that's exactly what I did the first day. I did, however, ride more than I had planned, riding the final 13 miles of the route, and so completing a total of 63 miles the first day.

I had plenty of strength to be able to ride the entire 74-mile course the second day. It was fun being able to do the ride with my friends, Ron and Eli. An experience like this is often more fun when it is shared. Here is a copy of the email I sent to those who donated to the MS Society as my sponsors:

Hello my friends,

It seemed so unlikely just a few months ago. As I stood in the staging area awaiting the 7:00 a.m. start of the ride on Saturday, I felt a combination of gratitude and determination. Gratitude that I was able to do the MS150 ride at all, after an awful health problem over the fall and winter, and determination to ride as well as I possibly could – not only for my own satisfaction, but for all who donated to the event.

Because of the longer course this year and the very long distance on the first day, I shortened my route on Saturday so that I covered 63 miles. Although it was difficult for me to voluntarily ride a shorter route, I knew it was the right decision.

Sunday's ride was warm and windy, and I was glad I had shortened my Saturday route. I rode the full 74-mile course, which finished to a grand celebration in Sundance Square in Ft. Worth. Nancy and some of my friends from work were there to greet me, and as I crossed the finish line to loud cheers, special mention was made over the PA system about my successful fund raising. The ride was very well staffed with volunteers who provided lots of snacks and encouragement. I have attached photos of my being greeted by Nancy, and raising my bike in celebration, soon after crossing the finish line.

The funds raised by the MS Society go towards research and to helping those afflicted with the disease with needed equipment and medication. Many of the newer medicines now being developed are biologic agents – antibodies against the specific cells and proteins that are involved in multiple sclerosis. This new class of medicines has revolutionized our care for all sorts of immune and malignant diseases. Their effects have been dramatic. As I have learned first-hand, one such agent is used in the treatment of lymphoma, increasing the chances for a remission.

In celebration of my being able to participate in this event and of my recovery, Nancy and I will again present bicycles and helmets to five 5th and 6th grade students from Hamilton Park, with the presentation "ceremony" at Richardson Bike Mart on May 20. The teachers at the school will choose the students, based on grades, citizenship and attendance.

Thank you all again for your continued support – support for me personally, and for the MS150 event – a very worthy cause!

I attached a couple of photos to the email – one of me holding the bike over my head in a gesture of victory. The other was of Nancy with me at the finish line.

As the teachings of Judaism gave me strength throughout my treatment, the symbolism of this being my 18th MS150 - my *chai* year, as I explained earlier – magnified the already raw emotions that filled me as I crossed the finish line.

I am grateful and thrilled beyond words to have been able to complete this ride and have asked for my oncologist's email so I can send him this note and the photos.

Thursday, May 7
Bar mitzvah anniversary and D'var Torah.

While understanding that no recovery is forever and that no victory in medicine is final, I am yet thankful beyond measure that my cancer is in remission. Medicine, family, friendships and connections, and Judaism have all played roles in my physical healing and spiritual strength.

Next Shabbat will be a special one for me. I will be chanting the *haftorah* – the same portion from the Bible I chanted when I became a bar mitzvah in 1964. Nancy and I will be sponsoring the Kiddush lunch, and I will be delivering the weekly *D'var Torah*. I have been working on this message for weeks.

Here is the message I will deliver in synagogue this Saturday:

Five Seconds on My Bike.
How Judaism Helped Me Cope with Cancer.

Seven months ago, I stood before you at the end of Shabbat services and told you that I had cancer and that an MRI showed that it had spread to my bone marrow. A bone biopsy that Monday would define the exact type of cancer I had. The only group setting in which I made such an announcement was right here. You have been there for me all along, giving me moral support every week. You provided plenty of "virtual" hugs on the days when direct contact was not allowed for me, and I came to shul wearing a mask.

I am, of course, grateful for the medical care I've received, and I am also grateful for my Jewish heritage and faith, which are responsible for some of the underpinnings of my emotional strength. The combination of good medicine, Nancy, and my shul has enabled me to heal.

So these underpinnings that I speak of – how exactly did Judaism help? What are the lessons and the points of emphasis of Judaism that helped me maintain emotional strength and helped sustain me?

There are five key features of Judaism that are pertinent here, the last of which will explain my somewhat cryptic title.

1. Judaism teaches us to appreciate the seemingly mundane.

Upon awakening in the morning, I immediately say a prayer. It begins with the words, "modeh ani," I give thanks. It is a very short prayer, in which we express gratitude for simply awakening and being able to live. As soon as I say this prayer, my mind moves along to what is in store that day. Instead of surveying how I feel and cataloging my bodily grievances, I think instead of what is to be done with my day.

Patients to see. Friends to reach out to. Spending time with Nancy.

*Judaism's emphasis on giving thanks for life – after all, we are taught in the Talmud to say 100 blessings a day – takes the emphasis **off** the negative. How extraordinary it is that Judaism encourages us to acquire a worldview in which nothing is taken for granted. We say prayers over food and for waking up in the morning. We even have a prayer upon seeing a rainbow. Not that adversity doesn't exist and needs to be dealt with. And let's face it – some days are just horrid. But for me, just being able to awaken next to Nancy – what could be sweeter than that? Just as pouring a few drops of milk into a glass of water colors the whole glass, a few drops of life's blessings can change the whole complexion of a day that might otherwise be filled with physical discomfort and emotional gloom. Judaism teaches us to "count our blessings."*

2. Judaism teaches faith and optimism.

This is certainly not original analysis by me – many of you have heard this before. When the Israelites crossed the sea after escaping their Egyptian tormentors, Miriam and the other women took out their tambourines and broke into song and dance. So there they were in Egypt. In such a hurry to leave, they couldn't even allow time for their bread to rise, so we celebrate with matzoh. Only the Jews would celebrate such a momentous event by eating such vile food as the "Bread of Affliction!" Anyway, on even the worst of my days over the past few months, I would tell Nancy at dinner that tomorrow would be better. That we would have the opportunity to play the tambourine again. Judaism teaches that tomorrow's events are not necessarily certain, and that we have a role in shaping those events.

3. Judaism emphasizes the importance of ritual.

The simple ritual of attending Shabbat services on Saturday morning, seeing friendly faces, and engaging in the timelessness of our prayers provided me with an anchor. That anchor's connection was both horizontal: to my friends and to other Jews who were doing the same thing at the same time, and vertical: the connection to what my ancestors did before me. It gave me peace and strength to feel the connection with Jews everywhere and at all times, knowing that even in illness, what I was going through was nothing different from countless others, and just as they do and did, I responded by my Shabbat morning ritual.

*The connection to my dear friends in the kehillah – **you** – gave me such strength! I typically planned D'vrei Torah the day after my chemotherapy treatment. And the very first time I led the P'seukei Z'mirot and Shakharit portions of the Shabbat service was also the day after a treatment. The mission to make Shabbat a special day, I'm convinced, gave me strength. And learning and preparing to lead those portions of the service after I was diagnosed with cancer added to my sense of mission.*

In Judaism, we know how special Shabbat is, and even if we have differing levels of observance, the day can still be special. My growth in davening and leading our shul in prayer was a response to the holiness of the day, and achieving personal growth even in the face of adversity is a traditionally very Jewish response. In my case, there was an additional benefit: practicing those portions of the service in the early morning hours before seeing patients helped take my mind off the symptoms that resulted from my treatment.

4. Judaism doesn't try to explain the inexplicable.

In Pirkei Avot, we read, "It is not in our power to explain

the suffering of the righteous or the tranquility of the wicked."
*I certainly do **not** mean to paint myself as a righteous*
person, but there is a larger point here. The Book of Job and
the Talmud teach that adversity and illness find us even
without our being culpable. I realize that many Jews would
disagree with my particular theology, but I don't believe
that my lymphoma was the direct result of God punishing
me or, for that matter, Nancy, or my daughter Leah. I also
don't believe it was the direct result of God teaching us a
particular lesson.

My feeling is that God created the universe and the rules of
nature, and disease is simply a manifestation of that. While
there may well be an overarching endpoint to God's universe
that I can't see and don't grasp, that would have seem to
have little to do with each and every individual occurrence
on earth.

The Torah, the Talmud and the writings all have the
same message – it is not in our ability to explain illness and
adversity. Although I do not view my illness as being divine
punishment, I can still accept the challenge of our faith
to continue to try to make the world better, act by single
act. I can even, if properly motivated, use the illness as an
opportunity to be an example of how to handle adversity
with equanimity, courage and the determination to continue
to do what I am called upon to do – as a member of my family,
as a physician, as a friend, and as a Jew.

5. Judaism is a culture of life.

Judaism doesn't much concern itself with angels, and we
don't emphasize heaven, hell and damnation. We can't know
what comes later, and we can't know what follows our lives
on earth. We can, however, affect the world, even if in a small
*way. We can help shape what comes next, and **that** is what*
Judaism constantly reminds us.

*Rather than a leap of faith, Abraham Joshua Heschel teaches that the Jew is asked to take a leap of action. We are taught to **not** accept suffering as God's will or God's punishment. We are taught to alleviate it. Every moment of life is sacred, and no act of kindness is wasted. Each moment of our lives provides an opportunity to do good – for us and for others. By changing ourselves we can change the world. In fact, our writings teach us that our mission is nothing short of tikkun olam – to heal the world.*

There is no glory in illness. We are told to heal the sick and to relieve suffering.

There is no glory in poverty. We are told to feed the hungry and to clothe the naked.

There is no glory in death. We are told to choose life. To preserve it. To make the best of it that we can, no matter the circumstance. And to appreciate it, extracting from it all the enjoyment we possibly can.

Last month, I actually had an experience on my bike that could be a metaphor for life and death, and for Judaism's message. I was riding early one Sunday morning. I came upon a red light and, of course, stopped. Next to me at the red light rolled up a man on a motorcycle. In the metaphor, my bike and I represent life; the man and the motorcycle represent death. There we were, side by side at the intersection.

I looked over at death and nodded. Death smiled at me and gave me a thumbs up sign, looking approvingly at my form of exercise and transportation. Life returned the thumbs-up sign and playfully called across the lane to death, "Wanna race?" Death smiled at me, as if to say, "Silly boy. You know I'm going to win this race. I always do." I, however, was determined. I looked back at the road, bracing myself for the race. My foot was in the toe clip, and I was ready to go. The cross light turned yellow. I gave a final glance both ways to be sure there were no cars trying to beat the light. The coast was clear.

The light turned green. Life was off to the race! I stood up from the saddle to gain more power. With several quick turns of the pedal I felt a surge of excitement and exhilaration. I glanced back over my left shoulder at death. The biker was just now entering the intersection. Life yelled out, in a really loud voice, "I'm winning!!!" Just then, I heard a loud VROOOM!!! And then, WHOOOSH – death passed me as though I was standing still. Death won the race after all.

By my estimation, I was leading the race for around five seconds. But those were five glorious seconds. Those five seconds in which life was winning the race were a tiny fraction of my whole ride that morning, much as our lives are a tiny fraction of the great sweep of time. But even with my hours of riding that morning, they were the five seconds that I remember the most. They seemed elongated in time, and I derived every bit of enjoyment I could while I was still ahead in the race. In reality though, the time was gone in a flash . . .

The Talmud teaches that when we die, we will face a heavenly court, in which there will be a number of questions for us to answer. They are, in my interpretation, whether we were honest in our business dealings, whether we set aside time for Torah, whether we tried to heal the world and whether we helped sustain the Jewish people. Elsewhere in the Talmud, we read of another question – whether we made time to partake of all the pleasures that were available to us in life. That is, did we appreciate the blessings in our lives and enjoy those that were accessible to us.

So my dear friends, pedal as hard as you can. The motorcyclist is revving his engine.

Shabbat Shalom

Epilogue

The epilogue of a book is a conclusion or summary of the main points of the book. As I prepared to write this epilogue, I was continually asking myself another question – a question that we should all be asking. What will the epilogue of my life be like? What would it say? How would its story be told? If my life ended soon, what achievements, events or personal characteristics would achieve the most prominence? Would an objective analysis tilt the scales toward more positive events or negative ones?

On the one hand, I lost my father when I was a small child, lost a college-aged son to cancer, and have had to deal with a very uncomfortable health condition since my early 30s. On the other hand, I have a strong and loving marriage, a wonderful daughter, have been afforded the opportunity to contribute to my shul and to many charitable causes, and for decades have been in a profession that has enabled me to derive much pleasure and satisfaction, while helping people. So have I been blessed or cursed? Like almost everyone, the answer is both. Still, the question persists: where will the points of emphasis lie when my life is over?

Judaism teaches that the answer to that question is mostly up to me. The narrative of my life will largely be personally determined, and will be decided by how I live my life. I do not believe that events are predetermined, and feel that we have free will to make the decisions that ultimately matter most, and to respond to events as we see fit.

There are some events for which there are no mitigating factors. Some tragedies are too horrible and too sad to respond to by saying, "Yes, but think of the bright side." In some situations, there is simply no bright side. Will the losses and afflictions of my life be so dominant that they completely overshadow my achievements and pleasures? Or will the goodness and worth of my life be sufficiently strong that I will have been shown to overcome loss and illness and to have lived a good and worthwhile life? It is up to me to affect the answer to that question.

With respect to my recent bout with cancer, was I terribly unfortunate to be afflicted with this illness, or was I blessed that despite such a serious illness, we have the medical tools to restore health? Where does the emphasis lie? I was unable to control the first part of the question, but am grateful for the answer to the second part.

There can never be a substitute for proper medicine and knowledgeable doctors to administer it, but other key themes run through the entire story of my cancer. I believe this chapter of my life reflects in many ways the other chapters. Support from family and friends, and a mission to get through each day with the will to do what I'm called upon to do were key factors in my response to illness – perhaps not necessarily in my medical recovery (for this, I credit my physicians and chemotherapy), but in maintaining an attitude of purpose, optimism and resolve. In so doing, I hope and trust this lessened my distress and the distress of those around me. Minimizing that anguish was essential to me during my entire course and has been similarly essential in responding to other instances of adversity I have faced.

In his book, *God in Search of Man*, Abraham Joshua Heschel makes a key point about religion in general and Judaism in particular. "Religion is not made for extraordinary occasions, such as birth, marriage and death. Religion is trying to teach us that no act is trite, every moment is an extraordinary occasion . . ."

Heschel teaches that our character and, ultimately, the worth of our lives, is determined by how we live. It is decided by our everyday actions. This is especially so in Judaism, where belief takes a back seat to deeds. Judaism is interested in the here and now. There is no glory in disease or poverty. We don't speak in terms of being "In a better place" after someone has died.

So will the narrative of my life be, "Although he was blessed with a loving family and a love of his work, he had to endure the early deaths of close family members and a chronic illness from the time he was a young adult . . ." In this sentence, the emphasis seems to be on the negative.

Or will it be, "Although he suffered through the early deaths of close family members and had a chronic illness from the time he was a young adult, he still achieved much in his life . . ." The emphasis here is on the positive. I strive each day to make this one the ultimate answer, with an emphasis on doing that which makes my life, those with whom I come in contact, and ultimately the world, better. I strive, in other words, to make every day count.

CPSIA information can be obtained
at www.ICGtesting.com
Printed in the USA
FSOW01n1814120915
10915FS